REPAIR OF ANCIENT BUILDINGS

TO THE MEDIEVAL MASTER-BUILDERS
AND THEIR MEN IN ALL TRADES,
AND TO MY MASTER,
MR. THACKERAY TURNER,
WHO HAS DONE SO MUCH
TO PROTECT THEIR WORKS FROM DAMAGE.

THE SOUTH AISLE AND TRACERIED WINDOWS OF HENLEY-IN-ARDEN
CHURCH, WARWICKSHIRE, REPAIRED BY THE TILE METHOD IN 1922

The effect of weathering should be noted. The photograph was taken
in 1928. When finished, the work was as bright as the finished
window of Limpsfield.

REPAIR OF
ANCIENT BUILDINGS

BY
A. R. POWYS

formerly
Secretary of the Society for the Protection
of Ancient Buildings

WITH

A NEW INTRODUCTION

AND

ADDITIONAL NOTES

1995

First published in 1929 by J. M. Dent & Sons Ltd., London & Toronto
and E. P. Dutton & Co. Inc.
Reprinted 1981 by permission of the copyright holder
Reprinted 1995

In this reprint photographs have been repositioned for
economy and in several cases are now closer to their
references than formerly. In addition blank pages and
chapter half-titles have been omitted; these are pages 1,
2, 8–10, 17, 18, 26–28, 37, 38, 107–108, 130–132,
150–152, 160–162, 170–172, 176–178, and 184–186.

ISBN 1 898856 01 X

Printed and bound in Great Britain by
Biddles Ltd, Guildford and King's Lynn

INTRODUCTION TO THE 1981 REPRINT

EVER since its founding by William Morris in 1877 the Society for the Protection of Ancient Buildings has had a particular philosophy. This can be summed up in the words "conservative repair" and is the antithesis of "conjectural restoration".

The basic idea is that ancient fabric should be disturbed as little as possible, the patina of age left on unscraped surfaces, and history not falsified by moving buildings to other sites or completing unfinished portions. When repairs are necessary they should be done with materials sympathetic to the existing structure but not concealed by artificial tooling, ageing, or staining.

We should approach old buildings humbly, being, as Morris said, "only the Trustees for those that come after us". Indeed the best attention we may pay them is to "stave off decay with daily care". Simple operations like keeping gutters clean, pointing sound, and woodwork painted, will maintain buildings at minimum expense for generations.

These ideas are today largely received knowledge. They were widely adopted only after fierce battle and long struggle by Morris's successors. Ideas and techniques were developed and refined by S.P.A.B. Committee members like Philip Webb, W. R. Lethaby and William Weir, as well as by Secretaries such as Thackeray Turner and A. R. Powys. The last was an indefatigable administrator from 1912 to 1936. So hard did he struggle to protect our heritage that his death at the early age of 54 is often attributed to over-work.

We are particularly lucky that A. R. Powys was able to write down "methods, in accordance with the principles of the Society for the Protection of Ancient Buildings, which may be employed in the repair of ancient buildings", as he says in his own preface to the book here reprinted.

In the many years since publication in 1929 methods have evolved, language has modified. Nevertheless, there is still no better summary of the Society's approach. Lethaby and Plunket Scholars attached to the S.P.A.B. every year have long sought out copies of "Powys" in rare-book shops.

The Society, in co-operation with Mr. Powys's widow Faith and his grandson Stephen Powys Marks, has decided to make an edition of the book available once more. This will fittingly mark the centenary of the author's birth.

We have reproduced the original text and illustrations exactly as they stand. Where details require modification we have added marginal numbers relating to corrigenda notes. In order to make the present edition even more useful to lovers and repairers of old buildings we have added some up-to-date information in appendices which have been prepared by Mrs. Adela Wright, the Society's Technical Adviser. These and the notes are printed at the end of the book, on pages 209–227. The following members of the Society have given assistance in compiling these notes: Mrs. Monica Dance, O.B.E. (former Secretary), Mrs. Penelope Adamson, Mr. Stuart Fell, Mr. Kenneth Reid, Mr John Schofield and Mr. Gilbert Williams.

Such details as availability of materials and refinements of technique alter, but they do not obscure the Society's—and A. R. Powys's—approach, which the Society for the Protection of Ancient Buildings considers will be as valid in its essentials a half century hence as it was 50 years ago.

David Pearce
Secretary of the Society for the Protection of Ancient Buildings
May 1981

A NOTE ON THE SECOND REPRINT

THE popularity of the 1981 reprint of this classic statement of SPAB practice shows clearly that its good sense and sound advice still have value today. No recent publication covers the same ground so well or in such a practical way.

We are therefore reprinting it for the second time. As before, the original text and illustrations are reproduced as they were printed in 1929. But we have taken the opportunity to update some of the notes added to the 1981 reprint. More importantly we have highlighted areas where practice has changed, principally in the conservation of wallpaintings. In A.R. Powys's day the application of wax was the generally accepted treatment. We now know this to have been a serious mistake.

Most of the examples given are English buildings. Specialist terms and building traditions do vary round the country, particularly in Scotland. These differences should be respected, but within the principles adopted by the society.

No book can be a detailed guide to every eventuality. Nor should it be used slavishly. But an approach based on the SPAB philosophy of conservative repair, given practical application by this book, should do much to ensure that we are good trustees for those who come after us.

Philip Venning
Secretary of the SPAB
1995

PREFACE

It is the purpose of this book to suggest methods, in accordance with the principles of the Society for the Protection of Ancient Buildings, which may be employed in the repair of ancient buildings.

There is no need to state these principles here at length; that has been done elsewhere. They are now well known, and are generally accepted. But in spite of a genuine intention to do repair work in accordance with these principles, fine buildings both Gothic and others suffer because they are mis-applied. I am therefore asked to put on paper technical information on this subject which has been collected by the Society during more than fifty years, for it was founded as long ago as 1877.

Stated briefly, the object of the repair work with which this book is concerned is to preserve and give renewed life to fine and old buildings that have been neglected or are decaying, and in so doing to avoid making reproductions to take the place of damaged features or missing parts when this involves the destruction and not the protection of what remains of the original work. Neither is this at all opposed to a warning which Professor Lethaby gave some years ago against making it a principle that "no work *which has to be renewed* should ever be put back in the form it had or in the material it was."

It is my experience that it is well to have this object constantly in mind when at work upon an old building; but at the same time I have found that it is not wise to lay down dogmatic rules, for when they are made one is apt to be confronted with a case where they do not work. I would therefore suggest to any who wish to understand the deep-seated purposes which are crystallised in the Society's principles and guiding rules, to study works both where they have, and where they have not, been respected. As examples of the former I advise that the repair works done by Mr. William Weir, Professor Lethaby, Mr. Harry Redfern, and Mr. Bowden be visited. I hope also that the same impulse to repair sanely will be felt to be the constant background of the advice given in this book.

The book is intended to be of use to all who have the care of valuable ancient buildings, or who are in any way concerned with their upkeep.

The architect may be disappointed that the advice given is not more precise, and the layman may complain that it is too technical. If this is so I would remind the first of these critics that each case must be treated as a separate problem, that he can expect to find nothing in the text of this book which will completely apply to any actual case. The advice is intended to be helpful in suggesting a right treatment, and not as providing dogmatic instructions as to the only way to proceed; and if the layman learns from the following pages that the difficulties are greater and the alternative methods more in number than he had thought, and therefore comes to realise what an infinity of care must be exercised in arranging for, and carrying out, such works, my two objects will be fulfilled.

The methods of repair discussed in this book are applicable to all sorts of domestic and church buildings.

AN ACKNOWLEDGEMENT

I WISH to thank all those who have helped me with advice and information to write this book. They are many. In fact, though the work comes from my pen, my part in it is small; for I have written here much of the traditional knowledge which the Society for the Protection of Ancient Buildings has inherited and gathered from many different sources. I don't pretend to have set down all that store of knowledge, and it may be that in some matters others would interpret it differently. It seemed, however, desirable that the information should be written out, and to the best of my ability I have done it.

The line drawings which are reproduced to illustrate the articles are by Mr. J. E. M. Macgregor, A.R.I.B.A., who made them in consultation with me. Mr. Macgregor has had practical experience in carrying out repairs.

CONTENTS

CONTENTS

LIST OF ILLUSTRATIONS

xiii

THE FIRST CHAPTER

GENERAL ADVICE TO THOSE IN CHARGE OF
ANCIENT BUILDINGS

The Purpose of this General Advice

Everyone will agree that the first duty of those in charge of fine ancient buildings is to keep them in structural repair. The second is to make sure that suggested alterations are indeed necessary, and to see that these are seemly.

The purpose of these general remarks is to show how these duties may be performed so that work may be done with the least alteration to the qualities which make a building worthy of notice, namely—workmanship, form, colour, and texture.

No Dogmatic Rules

At the outset, however, it will be well to state that no fixed rule can be set up to be followed invariably. Each case must be considered on its merits.

Hurry to be Avoided

It is also important that repairs to an old building should not be carried out hurriedly. Time should be allowed in which the effect of the repair of each section may be fully realised.

Order of Repair Work

It is not intended that works of repair should follow the order in which they are described in this book. The structure, however, should always be made sound before attention is turned to decorative features or fittings.

Preliminary Considerations

Those responsible for the treatment of an ancient building, realising that the contemplated work demands qualifications beyond their knowledge, will doubtless seek advice from an architect. It may be thought, having done this, their only remaining duties are to procure the necessary funds, and to enter into a building contract so that for a fixed sum the recommendation may be carried into effect.

Yet, as can be seen in many an ancient building, which has been dealt with under these conditions, such a course does not necessarily secure a building from harm.

Repair a Highly Specialised Branch of Architecture

Perhaps no branch of architecture calls for more highly specialised qualifications in all concerned than does that which has to do with the treatment of ancient buildings. The questions which have to be dealt with are of a most intricate nature, always involving the consideration of the twin needs of structural stability and of conservation, and sometimes also the making of alterations. In the course of work on an ancient building points difficult to decide and needing instant decision constantly arise. What needs renewal? How much may be retained? What technical method should be employed? and like questions confront one at every turn.

The Choice of an Architect, Supervision, and Workmen

In view of these, as well as of other considerations, the conclusion reached by the Society for the Protection of Ancient Buildings deserves close attention. That body holds that the ordinary methods of supervising works on ancient buildings seldom lead to the best results. It is essential that the choice of an architect should be most carefully made. He should be chosen for one reason alone, namely, that he has shown by actual work that he can repair an old building without doing it harm, or causing it to lose its value. Further, works of repair demand the constant personal supervision of a competent directing head. The appreciation of the merit of ancient workmanship, and its value as an archæological record is beyond the capacity of the ordinary Clerk of Works although his knowledge of modern building operations may be complete. Success depends on the actual handling of materials, and few workmen have the training and experience which enables them to act with certainty in these matters. It has been found, therefore, that if repair work is to be well done, either of two conditions must be observed. (1) The architect himself or else a competent, trained assistant should always be at hand whilst work is going on; or (2) the working-foreman in charge and the men he controls must be highly intelligent, and must have been trained in a tradition of sane repair under leadership such as is provided by the Society for the Protection of Ancient Buildings, or by the Ancient Monuments department of His Majesty's Office of Works.

It cannot be too strongly urged that much more depends on the skill of the workmen who actually do the work than in new building. If men, not specially trained, go ahead without waiting for detailed instructions, they may easily do irreparable mischief to ancient work which by skilled treatment may be retained: if they have constantly to pause for instructions, they are apt to waste time and become careless and, in the end, even if the work is successful, the cost will be increased in proportion. The men employed, then, should have so true an instinct for the right treatment of materials as to deserve the title of artist as well as that of mechanic. Many tradesmen, bricklayers, masons, carpenters and others, have it in them to work in this way, but owing to modern conditions of labour, and the fact that they work under many different architects who may have as many different conventions, they are apt to lose interest, and our ancient buildings suffer. Until a single sane tradition takes the place of fancy conventions, repair work cannot be done well without the special precautions which are recommended here.

The choice of a builder, if one is employed, has also an effect on the work, though this is less so than it was in the past, for builders tend more and more to become little else than financial agents.

In a word the success of the work depends on the men who do it. I write from experience; for working from a London office I have found it difficult to arrange to visit a building in the country more than once in a fortnight, and unless the men employed have the training described above this is not enough. In these circumstances if an architect succeed it is because fortune gives him workmen who know their job.

Contracts, Lump-sum or Other

A further point is that the execution of the work by a lump-sum contract is not in the interests of the employer, of the architect, or of the builder. Work on ancient buildings is speculative. The builder, if he be asked to do the work for a lump-sum, gives a price which he considers will cover him against possible loss. But, if the work should prove unexpectedly difficult, he is faced with the alternatives, either of doing work at a loss to himself and to his shareholders, or of doing only as much work as he can without placing himself in this predicament, less, in fact, than he knows should be done. Again, it is easier to estimate for putting in entirely new work, than for making repairs to the old. It is a fact that under the lump-sum contract, the tendency is for old work to disappear.

The undesirable features of working under a lump-sum contract may be eliminated if the work is done under "a schedule of prices" contract, or by the direct employment of labour and the purchase of materials by the owner through an architect acting as his agent. In both these cases payment is in actual accord with the work done.

Work carried out under "labour and material" contracts competently supervised, far from being more costly, as is sometimes thought, tends to be less expensive than work done under a lump-sum contract in the manner customary for new buildings.

Summary

As regards procedure, therefore, it has been found by experience that the best results are obtained when an architect is employed who is known to deal with ancient buildings in a spirit of conservation and is accustomed to work under a contract based on terms of labour and materials. He should be one who can give constant supervision, or who can get specially trained working-foremen whom he can trust in their various trades.

It is clear, then, that it is the duty of those who promote the work to assure themselves that proper arrangements are made before giving an order to proceed.

The Society for the Protection of Ancient Buildings can be of real service in advising owners and architects as to the arrangements which should be made for works of repair. It has great knowledge, gained from the experience of many men who have been concerned in the repair of ancient buildings. This knowledge it places at the disposal of any who may wish to consult it, whether they are architects, builders, or laymen.

THE SECOND CHAPTER

THE SURVEY OF AN ANCIENT BUILDING

A Thorough Survey Recommended

Those who have the care of an ancient building should possess a detailed survey of it. The survey should be: (1) written, (2) drawn to scale, and (3) photographic.

The written documents should contain an account of all the defects and weaknesses of the structure, and the nature of the materials used on the surface and in the core of walls and the condition of these. A clear account of the causes of failure should also be included. Further, there should be a description of repairs that have been or are being undertaken, and of changes that are made. And a survey can never be regarded as finally complete. It should be checked and corrected every five or ten years.

The survey made by drawings to scale should consist of plans, sections, and elevations of the whole and of parts; especial care being taken to show the position and extent of fractures in walls, vaults, etc., the irregularities that are due to movements, such as the leaning or bulging of walls and the sagging of horizontal courses. All these should be accurately shown on plan, elevation, and section. Superimposed plans taken at different levels are of great use. Figured dimensions should be fully given on these plans. When opportunity offers, drawings of hidden structural members should be carefully made.

The photographic survey should include views of the whole building and photographs of details; also, whenever possible, it should show the progress of building operations. This survey should be made to illustrate the written and diagrammatic surveys.

Such a triple survey should be kept up to date, and any movements that are discovered should be carefully recorded. The survey should pass with the building from owner to owner. It is remarkable how seldom even imperfect surveys exist on any but the most important buildings. They are in reality of great use, and the cost of making them, and keeping them up to date is small compared with their value. The Society for the Protection of Ancient Buildings has photographs and notes on the conditions of some buildings in England, chiefly of churches. But few of these deserve to be called surveys in the sense used here. They are always available for inspection. In its turn the Society would be grateful if this collection could be enlarged by the generosity of its friends.

When structural repairs are to be done a survey is always desirable and sometimes imperative. Too often the owners of buildings neglect to give instructions for this. It is true that an experienced architect can carry through superficial and sometimes even important structural repairs without making a record of such a survey, but this is no justification for its omission. They are useful, and will in the future be useful in the preparation of repair and strengthening schemes, and, incidentally, they may be useful to rebut criticism when such work is completed.

Mr. William Harvey, who lately worked under Sir Frank Baines on the staff of the Ancient Monuments department of His Majesty's Office of Works, is a strong exponent of the necessity for a thorough survey. His experience has led him to regard it as an essential preliminary to the repair of any large building. He has found that without it the causes of movements have been wrongly diagnosed. Mr. Harvey, for the first time in the history of the subject, has described what he has called "drift" in buildings. Briefly stated this means that wherever a thrust occurs in a building, unless it is met by the solid earth itself, gradually but inevitably the upright supports will be overturned: thus, if the cross or longitudinal section of a Gothic cathedral is considered, the thrust of arches against buttresses or towers high above the ground will, for all the precautional massing of weights at these points, eventually overturn them; and this in spite of the fact that when designed the line of thrust was brought within the central third of the bases of such buttresses or towers.   This is an interesting fact; but is one which, because the movement is very slow, may often be neglected or ignored for many long years in buildings that remain complete.   This is a point, however, to be noted in making a survey of all buildings, but particularly in ruins where counterbalancing loads and arches may have partly or wholly disappeared.   The best diagrammatic survey I have seen of any ancient building is the one of Tintern Abbey, which, I believe, Mr. Harvey prepared for the Ancient Monuments department.   A reproduction of this appeared in *The Builder* of 18 August, 1922.   The present movements in St. Paul's Cathedral are of this nature: there the great weight of the dome is causing "drift" outward to the ends of the transepts, the chancel, and even to the massive western towers themselves.

The necessity for the careful survey of even small buildings may be illustrated by a not uncommon state of affairs.   Walls of small churches have been condemned and rebuilt because when seen from within they have appeared very distinctly to lean outward.   A precise survey in such a case may prove that while the outer wall face is upright, the apparent inclination is due to the fact that the thickness of the wall decreases as it rises from the ground, while in reality the wall remains exactly as it was built.   It has been suggested that the explanation of the form of such walls lies in the fact that they have been built against the outer face of older and leaning walls.   In some small medieval buildings there is good evidence to support this explanation.

At Tisbury, in Wiltshire, there is existing a case of this kind, though I do not remember if there is evidence that the older walls were leaning, neither have I closely examined the joints between the newer and older work.   The central tower is twelfth century and no doubt the older chancel was coeval. There is now an early fourteenth-century chancel which may

well have been built immediately outside the old walls.   At
the west end of the chancel and to the east of the earlier tower
is an arch designed to carry the east wall of a tower that was
never built,   This is built against the older arch which still
remains.   It appears that the new tower would have been
big enough to enclose the old.

Points to be Noted

The following are points suggesting matters which should
be noted in making a survey:

The abutments taking the thrusts of roofs and arches should
be examined to see that they are strong enough.   Roofs which
have no tie-beams should receive particular attention.

Note should be made of all signs of damp in the building,
and their causes should be traced and recorded.

The nature of the site, the subsoil, the foundations and the
disposal of surface or ground water all deserve attention.

In dealing with church towers the particulars of the bells,
the cage in which they are hung, and the foundation beams
which carry the cage should be given with detail.

Provision against fire and any circumstance which might
prove a source of danger should be considered.

The nature of the various forms of decay that attack timber,
stone, and other material should be mentioned, and also any
evidence as to the rapidity and continuance of such decay.
For instance, in the case of timber it is important to notice
whether decay or weakness is due to dry or wet rot, to worm
or "shakes," and in the case of stone, whether disintegration
is due to frost, wind, or to chemically-charged atmosphere.
It may be advisable to take the opinion of an analytical
chemist on some of these points.

The dates of works of repair often indicate the amount of
movement which has taken place in a given period, and,
therefore, if possible, should be ascertained.

Fittings such as glass, tiled floors, brasses, statuary, and the
like should be described.

The Use of " Tell-tales " as Evidence of Movement

It should always be remembered that a survey is made as much in the hope of proving that extensive works may be unnecessary as of finding out what should be done; and with this in view the movements of walls, etc. as shown by fractures in them should be accurately measured and not assumed. As a means to this end "tell-tales" should be used. The usual "tell-tale" is of cement mortar about half an inch in thickness and an inch or so in depth placed across a crack after filling up any void, and extending on either side sufficiently to get a firm hold of the two solid portions of the wall. Tell-tales should only be set on firm material. Plaster is usually not hard enough to take them, and they must only be set on a clean surface, and no coating like limewash should intervene between them and the solid. Some advise that glass or tile should be used instead of cement mortar, as the latter material, unless in good condition, is liable to expand and contract when setting and so cause cracks which may be mistaken as a sign of continued movement. Mr. William Weir often uses Parian cement and prefers it to Portland cement for this purpose. There are also more elaborate and more scientifically accurate methods of testing movements which need not be discussed here. Besides scratching the date on the "tell-tales," note should be made on the diagrams and in the report of their positions and dates. Tell-tales should not be removed too quickly as it is useful to note if movement takes place during unusually wet or dry seasons, and whether cracks increase during and after repairs; indeed, where they are not conspicuous they should be allowed to remain permanently. Another advantage gained by the use of tell-tales is that movement may be shown to have stopped, and with this knowledge much work may be saved.

Calculated Stresses and Strains

In ancient buildings, while they are useful as a guide, it is seldom possible to rely on calculated stresses and strains except for quite simple forces, for the formulæ in general use are obtained by experiment in new work, whereas with age and decay the nature and strength of old walling varies immensely. Therefore the correctness of the conclusions is bound to rest ultimately on experience, for a number of important factors in the calculation must be postulated. Used, however, with proper caution they are helpful.

The Order of a Report on a Building

In writing a report on a building with a view to its repair, it has been found convenient to describe carefully its condition and the causes of defects before adding directions or suggestions for their treatment.

THE THIRD CHAPTER

TEMPORARY SUPPORTS, SCAFFOLDING, AND PROTECTION FROM DAMAGE DURING WORK

TEMPORARY SUPPORTS

Propping before Works

When a building is structurally unsound it may be necessary to support it with temporary props until such time as repairs may conveniently be done. It is the duty of an architect to advise on this, and to design the form of support to be used. Two precautions only are mentioned here as regards this matter. The first is in regard to the foundations for these props. They must be sufficient to take any weight that may come on them. They are usually laid on the surface and, therefore, must have a widely-spread base. The second is that it is advisable that provision be made to tighten up the support by wedges or otherwise.

Propping during Works

It is necessary to secure that no part of an ancient building is in danger of collapse during such structural repairs as necessitate the temporary removal of weight-bearing masses. It has become the custom to make the contractor responsible for the maintenance of the work during repair, but it is the duty of the architect to satisfy himself that the builder does provide efficiently against such risks, for in the case of an accident *ancient* work can only be replaced by *new*, and the whole object of repair work is to avoid this replacement. It is thus seen that more than financial loss is at stake.

When repair works are done by direct labour, the method always to be preferred, the architect in charge is more directly responsible for all temporary supports. This subject is too little understood by architects. It is also very difficult to describe in writing.

Kinds of Props

There are several kinds of temporary props. Those which act as buttresses are known as "shores." Those which support arches and vaults are "centres." Direct single props are   4 "struts." Horizontal pieces fitted across an opening, or between two walls to give them mutual support, are "straining-pieces." "Needles" are horizontal pieces passed through a wall to support it, having their ends in turn supported on struts; they are used to make it possible to rebuild the walling beneath or to make a new opening through the wall.

There are few operations in repair work which need so much experience, or which are so much governed by common sense, as the propping of old work during repairs. Except with regard to preliminary shores and the centering of arches, or with regard to those parts of a building where loads are concentrated, as, for instance, the piers under a tower, it is often surprising how slight the precautions may be. Round timbers, such as the short lengths of scaffold poles, are most useful as struts, for in these there is no risk that they are weakened by having had the grain of the wood severed.   5

Two Suggestive Instances

Two instances of temporary propping used by Mr. William Weir in the repair of a very shaky tower are given here to illustrate methods that are employed and to suggest others.

The tower in question was built of a limestone in the first quarter of the thirteenth century. The inner and outer faces would have stood well for a much longer time than they had done, had the filling or core been good. As a matter of fact the latter was as poor as it could be. The mortar had little lime in it, and the stones were small and showed little sign of careful placing. The consequence was that the walls were bulged and fractured in very many places. The top stage of the tower was built more soundly in the fifteenth century, but its added weight had further weakened the lower walling.

Before beginning work the whole of the lower faces of the tower between the buttresses was cased with inch boarding set vertically. This was held in position by heavy horizontal timbers set at intervals of about five feet. Tie-rods were passed right through the original putlog holes in the walls and passed right through the tower and the horizontal timbers, and the whole was tightly secured by screwing up the rods against any risk of patches of the wall face falling outward. The risk of falling inward was much less, and those places where any sign of failure appeared were secured during the work by straining-pieces across the tower. During the work the inch boarding was cut away in small pieces at a time as it was necessary to get at the wall face.

The walls were repaired by "building"; that is to say, by removing the loose core and replacing it with sound stuff. The work was done from the inside face through openings made at intervals. The difficulty was to maintain the very loose core above while this work was in progress.

The following method, with variations, was adopted to provide the local support required when these openings were made, and while they were rebuilt. Two stout squared timbers were passed at one level through the wall as needles, projecting from the inner wall face some two or three feet, and about three feet apart. At a suitable height above them, say four or five feet, two other similar needles were put. Upright struts were set just outside the wall faces from timber to timber and wedged tight. Lintel-pieces were sometimes put from one to the other of the upper needles under the facing stonework. Raking struts were wedged from the projecting ends of the upper needles to prop chosen larger stones of the facing some four feet or so above. Where the core was found to be dangerously loose further needles were passed from the inner lintel to the outer casing, and in some cases the hollows above these were filled with cement bags stuffed with hay to check the run of loose mortar and sand, of which the core was made. Thus secured from risk of a serious fall, each portion was opened and built up solidly, and the process was repeated as was convenient until the whole work was successfully accomplished. There are many modifications of these methods, one or other of which will suggest themselves to those confronted with similar problems.

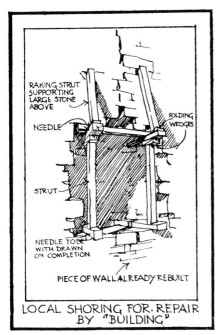

RAKING STRUT
SUPPORTING
LARGE STONE
ABOVE

NEEDLE

FOLDING
WEDGES

STRUT

NEEDLE TO BE
WITH DRAWN
ON COMPLETION

PIECE OF WALL ALREADY REBUILT

LOCAL SHORING FOR. REPAIR
BY "BUILDING"

FIG. 1

Constant Watching

One other word is necessary in connection with shoring. A careful watch must be kept on all "tell-tales" and the distances from the wall face to the plumb lines should be checked, and comparison made between these newly observed distances and those noted on the survey. Only in this way can it be known that the temporary supports are adequately doing their work. From time to time also the temporary supports themselves must be examined to see that they remain fit to take the loads they were designed to take.

SCAFFOLDING

The scaffolding for works of repair to ancient buildings should stand clear of the structure. It should have both inner and outer uprights, that is, it should be what is technically known as a "mason's scaffold." In such a scaffold the putlogs bear on inner and outer ledges and are not supported from the walling at one end. Such a scaffold is more expensive than a "bricklayer's" or attached scaffold, and, therefore, in special cases need not be insisted on. For instance, where old putlog holes exist they may be opened out and used again; where walls are of rubble and need complete repointing the extra cost may be avoided. But for ashlar work and in cases where a wall will be disfigured if putlog holes are cut, the attached scaffold must not be used.

A scaffold for repair work may be made with higher lifts or stages than is customary for new work. This gives head room on each stage and also makes for economy.

Scaffolding may sometimes be avoided when the work is light, by using instead travelling cradles. It should, however, be remembered that where the surface needs to be gone over many times before it is left, the time spent in moving the cradles becomes excessive, so that scaffolding is more economical.

A good deal of light work within reach of ladders may be conveniently done from "cripples" attached to them. For lower levels a plank-and-trestle scaffold is useful. A movable staging, sometimes made to expand, has been found convenient, particularly for use under cover.

PROTECTION OF FEATURES FROM DAMAGE DURING WORK

Precautions should be taken before any work is done to prevent accidental damage to the delicate features of an ancient building, and in conjunction with these, steps must be taken to ensure that those parts of a building designed to be under cover shall not be exposed to weather.

Protection from Accidental Damage

In the first case, statuary, carved and moulded stone or woodwork, glazing, whether coloured or clear, wall paintings and plaster work are among those objects particularly deserving protection. Cover boards properly fixed, match-board screens, wooden cases, and tarpaulin sheets are all useful in different circumstances with this in view. Roofs and pavements above which work is in progress should be similarly protected. A lead roof in the interest of economy alone, because it is peculiarly susceptible to damage, deserves such attention. Ancient work has sometimes been permanently damaged by stains of grout, of oak tannin, and of rust. The first is due to carelessness and should not occur. It can only be cured by immediate cleaning, the other two by keeping the work in the dry. When part of a building only is under repair, it is advisable to screen it from the rest to prevent the transit of dirt and dust. A lining of paper on either a canvas or match-board screen is an efficient protection against dust.

It is important that the men employed be told that the object of the work is to preserve and not to renew. In some cases they should be provided with felt- or rubber-soled boots. They must be cautioned against allowing fall-ropes to wear against beams or stone work.

Further, care should be taken to secure that no damage can be done by the movement or concentrated pressure of scaffolding, strutting, centering, or shoring on, or against, ancient stone-work. The pressure of such props should be transmitted over surfaces amply sufficient to receive it. Pads of felt, bags stuffed with hay, and tow-packing may be used to soften contact at these points. The ends of ladders should sometimes be provided with padded boards to increase the bearing.

Protection from Damage by Weather

When a roof is to be stripped for repair, or when a large window is to be left without glass, a temporary protection from weather should be provided. In the case of roofs it is advisable that a temporary roof be set up some five feet or so above the one to be repaired; it may be covered with tarpaulins, corrugated iron, or other suitable material. In some small works it is sufficient to spread a tarpaulin on the roof that is undergoing repair whenever work is not in progress. But in each case there should be provision for the discharge of rain-water well beyond the walls of the building.

THE FOURTH CHAPTER

THE DISPOSAL OF RAIN-WATER

Defective Rain-water Pipes a Chief Cause of Decay

Nothing, except a defective roof, hastens the decay of an ancient building so much as defects in the system designed to carry away rain- and surface-water. Most damp patches in a building which cannot be attributed to leaky roofs are due to leaky rain-water pipes. Therefore this matter should receive constant attention.

Generally speaking, buildings that are liable to long periods of neglect are better with only the simplest or without any system for rain-water disposal. In buildings in constant use the system should receive as much thought and attention as do the sewage drains from a modern house. The principles, however, are different.

For our present purpose it is presumed that the roofs are sound, and that only the disposal of water from the eaves downward is under consideration.

Systems for the Disposal of Rain-water

Water may pass to the ground by direct drop, either from eaves or spoutings, or it may be conveyed in pipes. In deciding which system is the better these questions should be considered: (1) Will the building be neglected when the work is done? (2) What is the nature of the soil on which it stands? (3) Are the eaves high above the ground, are the points of discharge well clear of the walls, and is the facing of the wall particularly liable to damage from more or less concentrated dropping water?

It may be that in the case of a low building with projecting eaves, and standing on a clay soil, the rain should be allowed to drip direct from the eaves to the ground, there to soak away. The advantages of this are: little initial cost, little upkeep expense, and the provision of evenly distributed water at the foundation-level, which may be useful in dry seasons, and

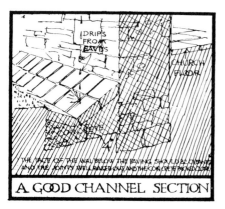

A GOOD CHANNEL SECTION

Fig. 2

which certainly avoids uneven contraction in the foundation bottom. In such a case provision may be made at the base of the wall to direct the splash outward. This may be done by a paving laid to fall steeply away from the wall at its base (see Fig. 2). It is sometimes wise to remove existing eaves-gutters and down-pipes.

Whenever water is concentrated at certain spots provision should be made by drains in the ground or channels on its surface to lead it well away from the building.

It may be in the case of a high building, as a tower, that a long rain-water pipe is undesirable because of the initial expense and because it is difficult to get at for repair. Further, rain-water pipes applied to buildings not designed to receive them may be held disfiguring. And in this connection lead pipes are better because they last very much longer than other kinds, and because they are more pleasant to see. On account of their durability they are good for buildings liable to neglect.

Down-pipes and Eaves-gutters

Iron down-pipes are more commonly used because they are cheaper at the outset. The following suggestions should be considered in regard to them. If they are fixed two or more inches clear of the wall, water from any leak that occurs will run down the pipe, and not down 'the wall. This is important because iron pipes are liable to fracture, and then concentrate water on a patch of walling much to its damage, and to the hurt of the fittings within. When down-pipes are fixed in this way rain-water heads should also have outlets arranged clear of the wall. Pipes to be fixed clear of walls should be round and should be without ears. They should be fixed by special arms known as "holder bats." When fixed to ashlar work these arms should be of gun-metal. To avoid fracture at the junction between two lengths of iron pipe the joints should be free, and in order to make repairs easy the upper length should only enter the lower by a little less than half the depth of the collar at the junction. This is done to make it easy to remove a defective length without taking down the whole pipe, for cracked cast-iron pipes cannot be repaired; renewal is imperative. It has been suggested that these pipes are best without any bends, and that therefore they should stand out from a wall as much as the projection of the lowest plinth. It is certainly desirable that no old work should be cut back to allow for their passage. A disadvantage of iron eaves-gutters and down-pipes is that they need to be kept painted. This is not so with lead pipes, which are always to be preferred. Where they exist they should be kept repaired; where they do not, it should be an object to put them in the place of others. They may be made of cast lead (seven pounds to the foot) bent round a mandril and the two edges burned together. Solder is often used for the joint, but a burned joint is to be preferred. The accompanying sketch (Fig. 3) shows a good way of fixing these pipes to an old wall. Lead pipes are usually fixed direct on the wall face, and they usually require heads which should also be of lead.

Both iron and lead pipes should discharge into a proper channel or above a gulley or into it by a back inlet so that they may be easy to clear at this point.

Where new eaves-gutters are used they should be of cast

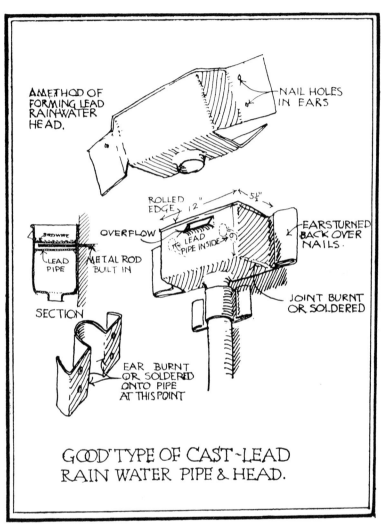

A METHOD OF FORMING LEAD RAIN-WATER HEAD.

NAIL HOLES IN EARS

ROLLED EDGE 12"

5½"

OVERFLOW

LEAD PIPE INSIDE

EARS TURNED BACK OVER NAILS.

BIRD WIRE

LEAD PIPE

METAL ROD BUILT IN

SECTION

JOINT BURNT OR SOLDERED

EAR BURNT OR SOLDERED ONTO PIPE AT THIS POINT

GOOD TYPE OF CAST-LEAD RAIN WATER PIPE & HEAD.

FIG. 3

iron, or sometimes of wood. When of iron, half-round gutters
are usually to be preferred on old buildings. Iron guttering
should be watched, as it is liable to fracture and, like defective
rain-water pipes, to concentrate water on a patch of walling
with dire results. A defective length of gutter should be
renewed as soon as it is discovered. Old lead eaves-gutters
should be maintained in spite of a pronounced disadvantage
which belongs to their nature, namely, that they are apt to
sag unless ample provision is made to prevent it. Wooden
gutters are out of fashion, but they are often suitable, especially for thatched roofs, for they can more easily be given a
form suitable to take the drip from thatch eaves, since these
vary considerably in projection as they age. Wood gutters
well made of oak or teak and well pitched within have a
long life.

The point where gutters behind parapets discharge into
rain-water heads is one where trouble sometimes begins. If
it can be arranged, there should be ample water-way here at
a level some six inches below the gutter, so that the outlet
may not get blocked. Chutes or spoutings from parapet-
gutters should have a like provision made. Where these are
high above the ground, as on towers, they should have a great
projection, to ensure that water does not drop on to offsets or
against the building. Some advantages belong to spoutings
which are formed as troughs and not as pipes. Lead spoutings
should be adequately supported to prevent sagging, and they
should have lips formed to pour the water clear and prevent
back dribble.

Disposal of Water at the Ground-level   7

Rain-water from roofs when it reaches the ground may be
disposed of in three ways. It may be allowed to soak direct
into the ground, either dripping from the eaves on to the earth
or on to prepared paving; it may drip from the eaves or be led
by down-pipes into open channels; or it may be taken direct
into drains from the feet of down-pipes. A building rising

direct from well-kept grass is beautiful; rising from channels
or paving it is perhaps less so. The means adopted to dispose
of water when it reaches the wall foot are further complicated
by the nature of the soil, by the level of the floor within the
building, by the nearness of paths to the building, and by the
fall of the ground. Unless drains are kept in order they get
choked and become useless, and this may become a reason for
avoiding them in cases where buildings may be long neglected,
as are some churches. In the case of inhabited houses rain-
water drains are less likely to be neglected, and are, therefore,

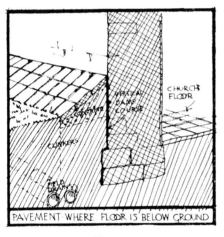

PAVEMENT WHERE FLOOR IS BELOW GROUND

FIG. 4

to be preferred as a rule.
The suggestions made
below must not be re-
garded as applicable on
every occasion; they are
no more than suggestions,
and should be used or
varied to suit each
separate case.

Where eaves drip on
to grass it may be well to
arrange for subsoil drainage by channels filled
with clinkers or broken
stones, or by agricultural
pipes. In the last case
the pipes should be continued well away from the building.

Where drains are not desirable, but where the floor is below
the ground-level, it may be advisable to lay paving sloping
outward from the foot of the wall. In some such cases the
wall below ground from its base to the top of the paving should
be faced with a vertical damp course. It may be desirable to
add a trench filled with clinker, etc. and grassed over at the
outer lip of the paving or, in some cases, at the very base of
the wall. (See Fig. 4.)

Where drains are desirable and eaves drip direct, or where
walls are severely exposed to wind-driven rain and there are

down-pipes, a channel at the ground-level may be advisable to conduct the water to gullys.

Channels or paving may be formed of concrete, but paving on concrete has advantages, and its appearance is generally to be preferred; paving without concrete is useless. Concrete set with kidney pebbles is good for channels, and may suggest other similar treatment. Both channels and paving are apt to set away from the wall, and every precaution should be taken to prevent this. It is most important to secure that walls against which the concrete is laid should be cleaned and the joints well raked out and the concrete well packed into the crevices of the stonework. For cleaning walling to receive a vertical damp course or against which concrete is to be laid, a stiff wire brush will be found useful. This is one of the few cases where wire brushes should be used in work on old buildings. Channels may be paved with selected brick or stone, and the choice should be made with a view to appearance as well as durability. It is a good plan to make the bottom of a channel more than half its width from the wall. Channels have one great advantage over drains: it may always be seen whether they are working well. This is important in buildings subject to periods of neglect.

In connection with this matter of channels, the custom of lowering the ground against buildings to a level below the floor should be considered. Where this is done the trenches should be wide, if possible three times as wide as they are deep. A narrow trench becomes foul and fills with leaves and refuse. It is the writer's opinion that it is better to provide vertical damp courses below the ground-level than to sink deep open trenches. But Mr. William Weir writes: "There is nothing so good as an open channel; it allows of air getting to the face of the wall."

9

Rain-water Drains

Where drains are laid for rain-water, the gullys should not be trapped, but it is an advantage that they should have catch pits. The gullys should have gratings, and these should be level with the bottoms of the channels. If they are lower than the ground near by, leaves tend to collect there and to block the gratings. The drains from the gullys should be laid with properly jointed socket-pipes, for they are otherwise apt to get choked with earth carried into them by worms or borne by the water. It is also desirable that they should be provided with access for cleaning. It is said that in clay soils agricultural pipes do not get choked. Rain-water drains should be laid where they are unlikely to be disturbed; in churchyards the lines of paths are suitable. Always a plan should be made of their course, and this should be kept with the survey papers.

The drainage of waterlogged soils is beyond the scope of this book. It is enough to remember that to rid a subsoil of its water is sometimes to cause settlements in a building.

THE FIFTH CHAPTER

MASONRY, BRICKWORK, AND WALLS GENERALLY

General

The aim in repairing old walls should be to make them sound and weather-resisting with the least possible alteration of form, texture, and colour.

The chief causes of failure in masonry, brickwork, and walls are:

(1) Want of regular attention.
(2) Percolation of rain-water.
(3) Foundation defects.
(4) Bad building up of materials.
(5) Unbalanced or excessive thrusts.
(6) Decay of materials.

Two or more of these causes may be present together.

Reference to the first and second causes has already been made in the chapters on "The Survey of an Ancient Building" and "The Disposal of Rain-water."

FOUNDATION DEFECTS

What to look for when Foundation Defects are suspected

Defects in foundations may be indicated by a drop or sag in horizontal lines as in string courses and in the bed-joints of the walling, or by walls which lean or are shattered or are cleanly cracked. These signs may, alternatively, indicate either bad building or the presence of excessive thrusts. Again, movements originally caused by foundation trouble may have ceased owing to equilibrium being reached later.

It is, then, necessary before making any recommendations to

make sure (1) of the cause of the defect, and (2) whether the cause is still active, for the treatment will vary accordingly. To find whether foundations are at fault a clear conception of the nature of the subsoil is needed and a precise knowledge of the bed on which the wall stands.   A peaty soil will compress, a plastic soil will both compress and squeeze outward, a loose sand will "run" if opportunity offers, and clay shrinks and expands as it becomes dry or wet, and may show a tendency to slide laterally. To obtain direct information about the subsoil, holes should be bored at a proper distance from the wall to such depths as may be affected by the weight of the building or into such strata as may cause changes in it.   To discover what the bottom immediately below a wall is like, holes should be dug at intervals along its length so that the bottom may be seen. The information so obtained should be immediately recorded and the diagrams and notes preserved with the survey papers. *This examination for suspected foundation trouble should be made as much to prove that no work is required as to discover what should be done, for alterations to foundations are liable to cause as many new defects as the old ones they cure.*

The following conditions in buildings and subsoils may suggest factors which will influence a decision as regards foundation stability If a subsoil is weak but is also homogeneous and if the conditions in it are unvaried and if the weight of the building is evenly distributed, there can be little foundation trouble. The reverse is what causes foundations to go wrong. For instance, the weight of a tower causing greater compression of the bearing soil may result in a fracture between the tower and adjacent work. Again, inequality of depth is also a contributory cause. On a clay site the part of a house standing above a cellar may remain as built, while other walls resting on a bottom nearer the ground-surface will move as the seasonal changes take place in it. A contributory cause of this movement is the fact that the concrete or walling of the lower foundation does not contract and expand in conformity with the movement of the soil on which the rest of the building stands. If the lower chamber is used for a furnace or boiler-house this condition may be aggravated by the tendency of the heat to dry out and contract its own immediate subsoil. In such cases, also, fractures occur between the parts. Excavations for drains, heating chambers, sunk roads, or graves, may remove lateral support at particular points or cause sand to "run" or changes in the water-level. The subsoil may be patchy and fractures be caused by changes in its bearing capacity. In short, when the foundation bottom is not homogeneous, where foundation depths vary or where saturation changes with the seasons, foundation trouble is likely to be the cause of movement in walling.

To make certain whether movement is still active, a prolonged survey is sometimes necessary, and in this case "tell-tales" are very helpful. With knowledge that movement has ceased much expense may be saved.

Treatment and Underpinning

It will be seen that there are two conditions under which foundations are adequate. The one when they rest on a bed that cannot move, as rock, firm gravel, chalk, etc.; the other when they are so spread on a homogeneous subsoil that no part of a building can move alone. Accordingly, the methods of securing defective foundations come under two heads. The one is to carry the foundations down to a rigid bottom, the other is to make inequalities negligible by spreading the foundations according to the bearing capacity of the subsoil and the weight that comes on it. The principle that no part of a building should rest on a firmer bottom than another underlies both methods. The object is not necessarily to prevent all movement, but to secure that the parts of a building cannot move separately. And even to this sound rule there are exceptions, for we find in old buildings a deliberately chosen compromise: namely, that parts of a building which differ in weight may be constructed independently so that they may move separately. Thus church towers are not

always bonded into the adjacent walls. In the marshlands
near the Wash, this compromise is carried so far that towers
sometimes stand several feet from the church. The provision
of a movement-joint is a common practice where additions
are made to-day, and where such a joint exists in an old
building it should very seldom be removed, and that only
after careful thought. Indeed it seems possible that the provision of such a joint might occasionally prove useful in repair
work, but because I know of no case where it has been made
during such work, the suggestion should be considered with
caution.

To put new foundations under an old building is to "underpin" it. It is a work needing experience and exceptional care,
if movement in the walling above is to be avoided. To underpin a wall it is necessary to mine beneath it; and even to do
this in small pieces at a time, which is the way the work is
done, may be risky if the wall above is not solidly built. Therefore, before underpinning a wall, the base, if not the whole of
the wall, should be made strong enough through its whole
thickness to stand the operation, for a wall should take its
own part in carrying its own weight across the holes as they
are mined beneath it. This strengthening may be done by
temporary props, or by permanent repair, and these methods
may be used independently or together. A technical matter in
underpinning further bears on a decision to strengthen the
base of a wall before the process is begun. The joint between
the new foundation and the wall above has to be very tightly
made. This is usually done by wedging up with slates.
Wedging up tightly is made easy if the underside of the wall
is even. Such a surface, if it does not exist, can be provided
when the base of the wall to be treated is strengthened.

During underpinning no opportunity should be missed to
insert a damp-proof course if one does not exist.

When it is decided to underpin from a rigid bottom that is
deep, expense may sometimes be spared by building piers at
intervals to support lintels or arches by which the wall itself
would be supported.

When it is decided to spread the foundations over a wide area, it is important to make the new foundation strong enough to distribute the weight evenly from side to side without breaking under its central load. In order to avoid excessive thickness and to save material, the modern practice is to use concrete strengthened with iron. Such concrete is known as ferro-concrete. On some sites it is found that one wall is slipping away from another, and in such cases the foundation slabs should be directly, and perhaps diagonally, anchored together, and for this operation also ferro-concrete is used. In extreme cases it may be desirable to put the whole building on a raft of this material, and this can be laid piece by piece in long trenches passing right across the building and beneath the walls.

It is important in all underpinning works that the new foundation should be continuous although it can only be laid in small sections at a time; therefore provision is made when each section is laid for bonding those which will adjoin securely to it. No two adjoining sections are laid in succession, time is allowed for each one to set hard before the next to it is put in.

Cases do occur where lateral movement alone is present, when in the place of a widely spread foundation beneath the walls it is sufficient to put a frame of ferro-concrete round them. In such a case direct and cross "anchor-beams" are almost invariably necessary to hold the framework stiff. Where lateral movement is on a large scale, as when the side of a clay hill is gradually moving down the slope, it is probably best to put the whole building on a strong raft of concrete, for then, although the building moves with the subsoil, it will do so as a single unit and the walls and arches will remain unbroken. Yet in such cases other means, such as piling or sheet piling, may be sufficient to prevent further movement of the subsoil. But where piles are used it must be definitely proved that the process of driving them will not jar the building to its hurt.

In cases where foundations are at different levels and

fractures have occurred at the points of change, it is probable that the only security against continued movement is to take the whole of the remaining foundations down to the same level as the deepest.   But this is an expensive operation, and it may be that to replace the fractures by the "movement-joints" suggested above would be useful.

To underpin a part of a building only, as a rule introduces one or other of the conditions which have been described above as causes of fractures in walls.   It is often tempting, but seldom a wise undertaking.   In fact, a faith in under-pinning as a cure for most ills from which walls suffer is to be regarded with suspicion.   Each case needs careful observation, sound diagnosis and the intelligent use of the appropriate remedial measures.

In practice, the expense of putting a building on a raft, or of surrounding the foundations in a ferro-concrete frame, often makes such works impossible.   In these cases it may be well to undertake local repairs only, knowing that it is unlikely that they will permanently resist future movement.   It is a perfectly reasonable thing to repair an ancient building to last a generation or two, leaving to our successors the duty of maintaining it in their turn.   The question in this case is to decide how the money available can be most efficiently expended.

DEFECTS DUE TO UNBALANCED THRUSTS, TO "DRIFT," AND TO BAD BUILDING UP OF MATERIALS

The Nature of Defects Originating Above Ground

Defects due to unbalanced thrusts occur where arches, and roofs have no tie from abutment to abutment, or are not supported by masses of masonry or buttresses of sufficient weight or stability.   They may also be due to the fall or disappearance of buttresses or counterbalancing arches or vaults. These defects may be recognised by the lean of a wall or pier away from the direction of the thrust, by the deflection of arches and the movement of archstones, and by the bending of piers and walls, with the consequent loosening or fracture of the walling near by, or the "sagging" of the courses of stone there. Where a timber roof without tie-beams is the cause, the joints of the principal trusses will be found to be open and the principal rafters bent or fractured.

Defects due to "drift" are of like kind, but pass from one end of a building to another; thus the mass of an arcade-supported wall may remain sound while all the columns or piers beneath lean away from the centre of pressure. Drift is usually caused by temperature movements. Expansion resulting from a spell of hot weather may cause a movement in one direction, and when the wall contracts again in cooling the resistance of gravity may prevent its recovering its original position and cause a fracture to occur. At each subsequent rise or fall in temperature it may happen that the fracture will open a little and will be further prevented from closing again by the fall of broken mortar, sand, or small pieces of stone in the crack. It will be seen, then, that movement due to drift is cumulative.

Bad building is due to poor mortar, or to the careless arrangement of stone or brick in it, or to both causes together, and these defects are more common in the core of a wall than at its faces. This condition may be recognised by the bulging and loosening of facing materials, by the displacement of individual stones, and by distributed fractures. Vertical cracks in the jambs of doors or windows give reason to suspect a loose and badly-built core. The crushing, spalling, and cracking of face stones of a pier or wall under direct loads indicate also that the core is probably poor.

When piers which are known to be of uniform strength are fractured or spall, it is a sign that they are eccentrically or over loaded.

Relating to Defects in Masonry, etc.

Where it is found that thrusts or drifts are becoming a danger to the life of a building, it should be decided how they may be made inert by work to be done within the walls of the building itself. Such a scheme may be put into practice coincidently with the repair of the fractures created by these movements, but the repair of the fractures will not be permanent until efficiently designed means have been taken to resist the forces that brought them about. In some cases there may be reason why these active forces should be met by new external and visible members which may be regarded as permanent props or shores. The overturning forces are so varied and sometimes so complex in their nature that an attempt to describe them here would take too much space. Before he determines on a scheme, the architect is advised to learn what has been done in other like cases. The English mediaeval builders tended to avoid the use of tensional members in building, and this may perhaps be said to constitute the chief difference between their and our methods. It will be found that the schemes for resisting the thrusts and drifts which are consequent upon their methods, often include the insertion of the tensional members which it is our custom to use in modern building. The insertion of these members may change the whole constructional idea of an old building, and by that very change harm it as an example of the old art of building; yet it may be that by such methods alone can the old form of a building be retained without external additions. It is known from experience that "drift" may continue for centuries before collapse occurs, and it seems that it is usually wise only to make use of these modern structural methods when a building cannot continue without them—and not before. It seems that until that time arrives we should repair an old building by the means that were traditional when it came into being, or perhaps only use our modern methods to repair single parts, always remembering that the time may come when the local work we do now may have to be linked to a scheme embracing the stability of the whole structure.

The modern material that has made such great changes in the constructive principles affecting our subject is reinforced concrete, a material which endures great compressional or tensional stresses alike. Though the time we have to judge this material by is short, it seems almost certain that iron or steel properly embedded in concrete is not affected by rust. But while any uncertainty remains this material, if used at all, should be used sparingly within the walls of old buildings. Ordinary iron and steel are not, however, the only metals which are available for this purpose; there are various alloys, such as "delta" metal, and both rustless iron and rustless steel, and while the behaviour of ferro-concrete is in any degree uncertain, it is wise, where valuable monuments are concerned, to use one or other of these metals as reinforcement. 12

There is yet another material which, while it is known to be certainly imperishable, is unable to resist the great tensile or shearing stresses which reinforced concrete will bear. This material is plain roofing tiles laid in cement mortar. Wherever the space within a wall is available, and the disturbance caused to the wall by its insertion is not too great, this material is recommended in preference to reinforced concrete. 13

It is the business of those who draw up the survey to search for and record the causes of failure, and to appraise their relative importance. It is not enough for them to see ponderous abutments or large tie-beams, they must find out whether these members are in fact still doing the work they were designed to do. Roof beams may stretch from wall to wall, and yet, owing to decay, their ends may no longer hold the wall-plates and thus withstand the outward spread of a roof. Buttresses, because they were built battering toward a thrust, may show no outward lean, but yet may long have ceased to perform adequately the purpose for which they exist.

It is not my purpose to make suggestions for stabilising the walls and arches of great buildings, but rather to discuss how this is done to-day in regard to those smaller works which too commonly need such treatment. The principles are the same, the scale of the work alone differs. In considering the more familiar we also inevitably refer to the unusually great. The repair of individual defects in walling, then, will be

considered here, and only by inference or brief notice will the
linking up of a whole building in a single scheme be indicated.

When a wall has failed, whatever the cause of the failure,
if still standing it may *always* be repaired by either of two
methods, used together or separately, namely by "Building,"
or by "Grouting under pressure." There is never need to
destroy, and thereafter to rebuild.

Repair by building is the process of rebuilding in small
pieces at a time those portions of a wall which are defective
and need strengthening.

14   Repair by grouting is the process of forcing into the crevices
of a wall a liquid mixture of cement and sand.

Each of these processes is described and explained in the
following pages. But first it may be desirable to warn the
amateur that it is useless to expect that a few bondstones
inserted in the face of a wall across a fracture, or that gravity
grouting will prevent an existing movement from continuing
to act. Such work is waste of money.

"Repair by Building"

A disadvantage of *repair by building* is that it necessitates
the disturbance of one face of that part of a wall which is
being treated. The great advantage of this method is that
everything that is done is seen and all material used is laid
by hand so that the adequacy of the work is evident.

The operation is usually confined to the course of a vertical
fracture, or to horizontal courses or belts of work designed to
give a weak wall strength in direction of its length either to
resist tensional, compressional, or shearing strains.

The first matter to be settled in repairing a wall by *building*
is from which face the work is to be done. On this may
depend the arrangement of scaffolding or shoring. One face
may be preserved undisturbed, and it should be chosen because of the value of the original workmanship it shows, or
because of the interest it derives from the mellowing effect
of age. Ancient plaster usually has preference over rubble

facing, not only because new patches in plaster tend to show afterwards, but also because plaster often bears valuable traces of colour decoration. Panelling which can be easily moved affords an opportunity of access to a wall which, when the work is finished, it will again cover.

In the repair of a fracture the object of the work is to unite the two sound parts of the wall throughout its thickness so that it may again be a single unit. The work is begun from the bottom of the fracture. Here the loosened walling is cut out on either side of the fracture, and a hole is made into the wall from the chosen face to the back of the stones which form the other surface. In cutting the hole these stones must not be shaken. The height of the hole should be such as is convenient for one man to work in a single lift, its width should be regulated by the amount of supporting masonry which may be safely taken out at a time, and by the extent of the weakness in the wall. The question of shoring or propping the work above during this operation is referred to under that heading, but this also will influence the size of the hole.

The tools used in cutting such a hole are a crowbar, a small handpick, and a hammer and chisel. Except where it is necessary to remove sound walling to obtain proper bond, loose walling only should be removed. Care should be taken not to jar stonework that is to remain; this and the stonework above should be examined from time to time to see that no movement is taking place. When the hole is ready, but before new material is put in, the sides and back must be plentifully washed out with water. A hose or a garden squirt is useful for this. Again, before new walling is built up, crevices should be grouted by hand; it is also good to fling grout into the sides and back of the hole. Any materials that are sound and which may be convenient can be used for refilling. The usual practice is to build up the facing with the best stones taken from the hole after they are cleaned, coursing the stone like that adjoining. In special instances the face stones should be replaced just as they were found, and for this purpose the stones may be numbered, photographs taken and careful drawings made before the work is begun. The rebuilding is done in heights of one foot to eighteen inches, the lower courses tailing back into the wall as far as may be. The core of the wall may then be filled in level with well-packed concrete, and in this concrete may be bedded clean old stone, tiles or brick. At intervals it may be well to lay a course of flat stone or tile on the concrete to steady it, and to form a sound bed for the next operation. When this work is stiff enough the next section may be built and so continued until the hole is built up and the two sides of the crack properly bonded together.

Although it is not desirable that the ingredients used for concrete or their proportions should be described here, for that may be found in many books, it is worth noting that the aggregate is improved by a proportion of broken brick, for this material being porous will absorb water, which it gives up to lime or cement during setting, to their great advantage.

Great care must be taken to see that the pinning up to the walling above is well done. Pinning up should always be done from work that has set firmly, and it is usual to build the final courses of the filling with brick, tiles, or flat stones to form a base to work from. The actual pinning is usually done with brick courses between which pieces of slate are driven until they are so tight that the joints will take no more. If lime mortar is used for the general walling, the final courses are usually built in cement mortar so that it will set quickly. It may be found convenient when the facing is of flint to use board "shuttering" across the face of the hole, and to fill in behind completely with concrete, but if this is done the facing flints should be laid by hand against the boards as the work proceeds; or alternatively the flint face may be bedded in and thereafter held in position by boards while the concrete is put in. In such work it is sometimes desirable to lay steadying courses of tiles across the body of the work at each lift. These tiles need not show on the face.

It may happen in conjunction with this work that it is advisable to build belts a little way into the wall on either side of the crack, or, if the wall is loose and needs long horizontal ties, for considerable lengths. This is done in the same way in small sections, but each section is built so that the next may be bonded to it to give the whole belt tensional strength; and when one section is complete the adjoining work is not opened out until the first has set firmly. The forces to be resisted by a bonding course are different from those which are provided for in building up a crack. Such belts are inserted as horizontal ties, and for that purpose should have great tensional strength. It is Mr. William Weir's practice to build these belts in specially bonded brickwork, or with plain roofing tiles laid as bricks. It is the practice of the Ancient Monuments department to build them in ferro-concrete. When brickwork is used every course is laid as a stretching course, and the bond from back to front may be broken by building every alternate facing course with three-quarter bricks laid as headers, or, when the brickwork is faced with other material, the bond is easily arranged within the wall. Plain tiles are laid on the same principles, and where these are used, tiles made by hand are the best for the purpose. All cracks may be repaired in this way or by using modifications of it. Thus it may be decided that it is unnecessary to rebond the crack from bottom to top, and that it will be sufficient to put across it at intervals bonding blocks or stitches of masonry or tile. It must be remembered that these stitches should tail well into the sound wall on either side and that they should go through the thickness of the wall to the back of the facing which is to be preserved. In such cases the intervals between the stitches will be repaired by grout poured in by hand or pumped in under pressure.

A wall of which the core is loose throughout may be repaired in a similar way; as a rule, in such cases the repair will be done by building belts at intervals, and by grouting up the work between them, and to this system may be added a series of vertical strengthening members built into the wall in the same way as is done when a fracture is repaired. It may be argued that it would be easier to rebuild the wall completely, and indeed this might be so. But if the object is to preserve ancient work, or at least the ancient lines, and one face of the walling complete, such procedure would altogether defeat that object.

Always when repair to walling is done, whether, by grouting or by building, the quoins and angles of walls, windows, gables, parapets, etc. which, by their lines, give the building its characteristic form should remain undisturbed. This may be more easily recognised as essential when a mediaeval spire with its irregular entasis and sometimes slightly twisted shape is considered. In rebuilding, entasis may with difficulty again be given it, but it is impossible to recapture the lines which, as modified by time, an ancient spire has acquired. The masonry, brickwork or other material which form these important lines may be made firm, given new beds and new backing, may be rebonded to the wall without even temporary removal or interference, by the simple method of working first from one side and then from another. Half a bed joint may be cleaned out and renewed, and when this has set the other half may be treated likewise. The brick-built turret-tops of West Stow Gatehouse (see Fig. 5) which were rotten with vegetation were so repaired by Mr. William Weir. The photograph of this work shows how impossible it would have been to have rebuilt them in their old form had they been taken down. The crocketed angle ribs there are of small pieces of modelled brick or terra-cotta; each was entirely rebedded and rejointed, yet none was lifted from the place in which it was found.

Instances of parts of buildings which have been successfully repaired by these methods could be given again and again almost without number, but one other only will be mentioned here in illustration, the repair of the broken chancel arch of the parish church of Hanborough, Oxfordshire (see Fig. 6). In such a case the procedure is as follows: The arch is properly centred and the scaffolding is erected; it is decided that the work should be done from one or both faces; the walling immediately above the arch is removed in small pieces at a

FIG. 5.   WEST STOW HALL, SUFFOLK, AFTER REPAIR, 1906

Fig. 6. Hanborough Church, Oxon, Chancel Arch During Repair

time from the very springing or otherwise as may be necessary, the backs of the arch stones are cleaned, and for this a wire brush is useful, and the joints refilled with mortar from the top; a relieving, or new, arch is built above the old, and the walling over that filled in again and pinned up to the work above. When the whole of the arch has been treated piece by piece in this way, a bonding belt which may be cambered in itself is put in above the crown of the arch extending across the width of the void below; finally, the wall face is replastered and except for this fact no change can be seen.

It may be noted that it is Mr. Weir's custom to use the method I have named "repair by building" whenever this is possible, rather than "repair by grouting." The author of this work is convinced that he is right to do so.

"Repair by Grouting"

It has been noted that *repair by building* has one disadvantage, namely, it necessitates the disturbance of at least one face of the wall under treatment. *Repair by grouting* makes even this disturbance unnecessary. But it is the opinion of the author, an opinion that he believes will be confirmed by all but ardent supporters of this method, that *repair by grouting* can never be relied on as confidently as repair done by building. Grouting is, however, certainly most useful when used in conjunction with building.

Repair by *grout* pumped under pressure from a special grouting machine was first used on ancient buildings by the late Sir Francis Fox, and in his more recent works he devised a method which partially overcomes its chief disadvantage, that is, its want of tensional strength; this he did by joining to it a system of tie-rods of "delta" metal. In this way, with Sir Charles Nicholson, he repaired the western towers at Lincoln, and in this way at the present time an attempt is being made to repair the piers which support the dome of St. Paul's. 16

Before the actual grout is pumped in, preparation should

be made to receive it. Cement will not set to dirt, and if the sides of the crevices into which the grout is forced remain dirty it will do very little good. Further, grout pumped into dry walls is liable to surrender its moisture to the porous core of the fabric and be thus deprived of its setting power. Therefore the crevices and voids which are to be filled must first be cleaned by being blown and washed out. In cases where the inside or core of a wall is very loose, care must be taken to see that only the dirt and dust are removed, and it may be necessary to provide shores or sheeting even with this method. Loose joints in the masonry which can be got at from the face of a building should usually be cleaned out deeply by hand with hoop-iron or other implements. Sometimes this part of the work is better done separately before grouting is begun and sometimes after it is complete. In any case all possible exits should be stopped either by permanent pointing or with clay. When all is ready the nozzle of the hose from the machine is put into specially prepared holes at the base of the portion to be grouted and the grout is pumped in at pressures which are usually wisely kept down as low as twenty-five pounds per inch. After the grout has set a little the hole by which it entered may be cleared, and later when setting is complete the grout may be pumped in a second and third time using increasing pressure. When this has been done the holes drilled to receive the grout may again be cleared, and the reinforcing bars may be put in them and bedded solid in cement mortar. This operation is then repeated throughout the wall, working from the bottom to the top.

Grout cannot make old poor material into sound new mortar, all that can be done by this method is to fill the voids. In actual practice these are usually the spaces made by vertical or raking fractures, and they occur just where the stresses are greatest. Grout without reinforcement does little more than turn these fractures into long cement-filled, continuous joints, and these long vertical joints are just those which every architect knows are undesirable because they are very weak. They would never be allowed in new building. Further, the

grout itself can only set on to the old mortar and stone filling
which has already shown that it is not strong enough to withstand the strain that has come on it, and although the new
cement itself may remain sound, these old materials may again
break away from the newly-formed continuous joint. Thus,
it will be seen that while movement is active, while "drift"
remains unstayed, grouting under pressure will not render an
old broken wall sound. It is only really useful when movement has stopped, or is held, that is, when the main forces
have been countered by *repair by building*. And as to the
reinforcement, this cannot be inserted longitudinally in a wall
except with much disturbance amounting to *repair by building*, unless unusual opportunities like lateral passages occur.
Grouting can, however, be very useful to stabilise a wall which
is to undergo underpinning or *repair by building*, and if the
destructive forces are met by building methods at the vital
positions, grouting for the remainder of the wall which is thus
brought into equilibrium is excellent.

Hand-forced grout is only useful for filling the joints between
individual stones, and grouting by gravity from a raised tank
has been found impracticable for serious repair works.

Grouting machines can be hired from those firms which are
accustomed to carry out repair works on ancient buildings.

Repair by Permanent Props—Buttresses

It is a common practice, when a wall is seen to be weak or
leaning, to recommend the building of buttresses, and it may
be that this is sometimes desirable. But there are disadvantages to this way of strengthening buildings. First among these
is the fact that the original form of the building will be altered
thereby: and as the object of repair works is to preserve works
of ancient art and craftsmanship complete and unaltered, such
additions should only be made when the building to be repaired
is shown to have been defective for want of these features, and
not because the walls are badly built or have become defective.
It is a rule that buildings should always be repaired by

strengthening the walls rather than by adding to them. The case of a ruined building or one which has lost important constructive features is different, for in those cases it does sometimes become necessary to build additional supports to take the place of what has gone.

There are also structural difficulties in building new buttresses which, although they can be overcome if proper precautions are taken, render it desirable to avoid building these features. It is constantly repeated, and as often in practice forgotten, that a new buttress set on virgin soil will settle considerably, and in doing so will either move away from the wall it is built to prop or will hang from it by the bonding stones which unite it thereto. In the one case the buttress is useless, in the other it is an additional burden to the wall. The examination of buttresses built under these circumstances will seldom fail to show movements of the kind described here.

If, then, it happens that external support by buttressing is thought desirable, certain precautions are necessary.

First, the foundations should generally be made on the same bottom as that on which the building stands, so that movement originating there may be uniform. A widely-spread concrete footing is usually very desirable. There are two forms of buttresses, the one attached to the supported wall throughout its height, the other an arched or flying buttress. When an attached buttress is chosen it should be built in quickly-setting mortar, that is, in cement rather than lime mortar. The bondstones should be built in the old wall independent and clear of the new buttress though in the same plane, and should be of stone or of concrete which will withstand great shearing stresses. Standing on the new work and beneath the new bondstones at each stage powerful jacks should be placed and screwed up from time to time so that the new buttress may be compressed under the actual weights it will have to take when complete. These jacks should be left in and screwed up as may be necessary from time to time until settlement in the new work may reasonably be held to have stopped. Then, and not till then, the jacks should be removed, and their position taken by solid walling properly pinned up from the new work to the bondstones.[1] One other precaution should be taken within the wall itself. It should be ascertained that the walling about the bondstones is sound and strong enough to pass the weight that is to be taken by the buttress.

An advantage of the flying buttress is that by its very nature it will lean against the wall to be supported even if the foundations on which it stands do subside a little. Such a buttress, unlike the other kind, is best built in lime mortar so that it may be able to adjust itself during the months of setting, which is the period when movement in the foundations will principally occur.

Other forms of permanent shoring should also be considered here. The well-known arrangement including an inverted arch which stands beneath the central tower in Wells Cathedral is little else than a permanent shore designed on the same principle as those temporary timber straining-pieces which are so often used to support one wall or building from another during building operations. With such precedent before us it may sometimes be well to consider building such support again, but in doing so it is not necessary to adopt for these the same features which are used at Wells or in the chancel transepts of Salisbury Cathedral. Indeed these forms, though fine and reasonable as examples of technical skill in the mediaeval tradition, would justly be described as clumsy if carried out to-day. In such circumstances other light but equally efficient constructions may possibly be wisely designed and employed.

There is yet another form of permanent visible support which may be used, namely, iron tie-rods and timber beams. I have already pointed out that mediaeval builders preferred to put their structural members in compression rather than in tension. Abroad, such members are comparatively common. There are, however, well-known instances where tie-rods and tie-beams are used. At Westminster Abbey the

<hr/>

[1] I think this method was first suggested by Mr. William Harvey.

original iron tie-rods remain at the springing level of many arches to resist their spread. Professor Lethaby tells us that the Chapter House vault was in the thirteenth century held in place by these means. Many timber roofs were designed with tie-beams, though the large timbers that were used in this position suggest that they were also designed to resist compression, and thus to act as straining-pieces. We know well the advantages of such tensional members, but in the repair of old buildings we tend to be shy of their use. The Westminster arch-ties are stout iron bars, square in section, made with eyes at the ends to pass over hooks built into the masonry as the work rose up. When such rods are inserted into old buildings it is well to see that the hooks are of rustless metal, on the accepted principle that iron and steel should as far as possible be excluded from old walls.

Cob and Clay-lump Walls

Cob and clay-lump walls are difficult to repair. These materials are not lasting unless certain conditions are observed; and the conditions should first of all be examined and made right. These walls must be well roofed, and the roofs should have well-projecting eaves. The exposed wall faces must be protected from weather, either by plaster, by repeatedly applied coats of limewash, or sometimes by tar. When a clay-lump wall has become decayed it may be repaired by removal of the defective lumps and by the insertion of new. When a cob wall is decayed the case is not so simple, because freshly-made cob cannot easily be made to adhere to the old, and because when the old is cut out and new cob inserted, it cannot be rammed in tight as underpinning is done, and, further, it shrinks very much when drying out. A cob wall may be repaired by cutting out the decayed part through the thickness of the wall, by arranging an even bed to pin up to, and by rebuilding the opening with ready dried and shrunk lumps specially made in the same manner and from the same material as was the wall.

Half-timber Walls

Oak-framed walls are generally known as "half-timber work," though they deserve equally to be known as "timber and brick" or "timber and cob." The repair of timber framing is discussed later; but it is not out of place here to refer to the filling between the framework.

The variety of the filling found in timber framed buildings seems to be due to changes in the materials available for the purpose and the convenience with which they were used. It is a matter closely related to building economy, as indeed are all changes of method and material. Originally it was general to fill these spaces with wattle-and-daub, a material which has not great lasting qualities when exposed to weather or hard wear, but which could in old days be easily renewed with but little cost. When bricks came into general use they supplanted wattle-and-daub, both in repair work and in new building. As a consequence we find to-day both methods in use in one building. Sometimes the upright timbers had less thickness than bricks; and in such cases, when repair with bricks was done, they were allowed to project clumsily beyond the framing; but because the bricks used in these repairs are often of a fine quality both as regards their texture and colour, they should not be removed. It is very seldom necessary to remove and rebuild brick filling for repair; it should be the object of those concerned to make the wall sound without doing so. Brick filling that has moved out of position can be pressed back into position, though to do this it may be necessary to clean and remake the joint between brick and timber. This joint may be made with mortar; but it has been suggested by Mr. F. W. Troup that the joint could sometimes be remade by using caulking as is done between the planks of a ship's deck. This method would have the great advantage that such a joint will expand and contract to some extent, and so allow for the slight swelling and shrinking of the timber during changing climatic conditions. Although most people know that the custom of building the brick filling with diagonal mortar joints was done to encourage the bricks to press tightly against the timbers while the mortar was still soft, there are still some who imagine this custom is derived from a desire to add interest to the appearance. With this knowledge it is easier to resist the temptation which some repairers have to make patterns in the brick panels they renew instead of maintaining.

External Plaster on Timber Framed Buildings

In the eighteenth century it became the fashion to apply lath and plaster to the outsides of timber framed buildings. This was done for two reasons. The first was due to the greater standard of comfort enjoyed then, for timber framed buildings are apt to be draughty and everyone knows a brick wall only four and a half inches thick does not keep rain out. The second reason seems to have resulted from the fashionable outlook of that day in regard to old work. It was little respected. Half-timber work seems to have been regarded as a poor way of building and was covered with plaster, because it did not then show, or at least did not display this supposed sign of poverty. Most of the plaster-work applied for these reasons was of excellent quality and was often well modelled and patterned. Further, it hid the changes that were made at about the same time in the shape and size of the windows. It is a mistake to assume that the plaster should be removed, and that the building should be restored to its older form. With the removal of plaster a variety of difficulties arise, much "Restoration" usually follows with the disagreeable results we are accustomed to associate with similar work done in the nineteenth century or with the imitation Tudor architecture of the Earl's Court and Wembley exhibitions. Plaster should only be removed from half-timbered buildings when it is valueless as an example of craftsmanship, when it is harmful to the structure, or when it must be removed to enable repairs to the timber framing to be done. The difficulty of keeping wind and water from driving through these walls is further evinced, for other means also were commonly taken to keep them out. Both weather-boarding and tile-hanging are often found on such buildings. In every case it is wiser to approach the problem of repair with a strong prejudice in favour of these coverings than with a conviction that because they are later work than the framing they should, therefore, be removed.

When it is desirable to maintain the old lath and plaster on timber framed buildings, either because of the fine modelling, or for other reasons, and when this plaster is bulging or loose because either the lath or the lathing-nails have decayed, the following method may sometimes be used with success. The plaster may be screwed back to the upright timbers or to smaller crosspieces specially inserted from the back between them. If a screw-head is not big enough to hold the plaster alone, then to secure it, zinc or copper washers about the size of a penny may be sunk into the plaster and screwed up. Brass screws may be used. If a patch has bulged very much, care must be taken not to crack it when it is again pressed home to its original place. The counter-sunk screws and washers are covered with plaster and so do not show. Further, it is possible, when the plaster is pressed back into position, to reinforce it from behind with a new plaster backing, strengthened with canvas and fixed to the stud work, as is done in the case of valuable modelled ceilings.

Tile-hung Walls

Like plaster, the tiling of wall faces should as a rule be maintained. And this is no difficult matter, for this work is done in much the same way as when tiled roofs are repaired. Care should be taken in regard to such new tiles as may be wanted. These should be made by hand in the same way as the old, and of the same size and shape.

An uncommon form of tiling was sometimes used in the south-eastern counties of England in the late eighteenth and early nineteenth centuries, namely, a tiling designed to look like brickwork. Where this work exists it should be repaired, and new tiles made to take the place of deficiencies. The 18 accompanying sketch (see Fig. 7) will illustrate the form of tiling. It is usually found in conjunction with a "brick-nogged" wall, and the tiling nails are driven into the brick joints and into the upright timbers. On a vertical wall this tiling forms an excellent protection from the weather, and being properly bedded in mortar and without exposed edges, it cannot be damaged by a ladder carelessly leant against the wall face.

The repair of weather-boarding also deserves some mention. It is a safe rule that the form of weather-boarding that is found should be again adopted when renewal or repair is done, unless it is such as will encourage decay in itself or in the framing which carries it. Not very long ago painted deal boarding was almost invariably condemned, not because it was decayed, but in the belief that it was incorrect or ugly, and a fashion arose to substitute for it weather-boarding of elm on which was left the irregular edge often with the bark still on it. It is a pleasure to know that this fashion has now died out, though unfortunately the suburban builder still follows the bad example that was set. If there is no reason why other forms of weather-boarding should be chosen, oak, chestnut, and elm are good for the purpose, but in all cases the boards should be cut straight. This was the custom in all old woodwork except where even the cost of an extra saw-cut was a waste of money, as in the meanest farm-buildings, pigsties, etc.

The lighter kinds of slate hung on wall faces were and are used to withstand rain. At Exeter and at Ashburton in Devonshire there are beautiful examples of slate-hanging, patterned with shaped and coloured slates, deserving most careful preservation. But old walls which have been covered with the large thin smooth slates should be stripped, and the walls made rain-proof by some more appropriate means.

Where the wattle-and-daub filling between the timbers is so deteriorated as no longer to resist weather, or where it has disappeared, it is often the custom to substitute concrete for it. When this is done the following precautions should be taken. In early work the sides of the upright timbers were

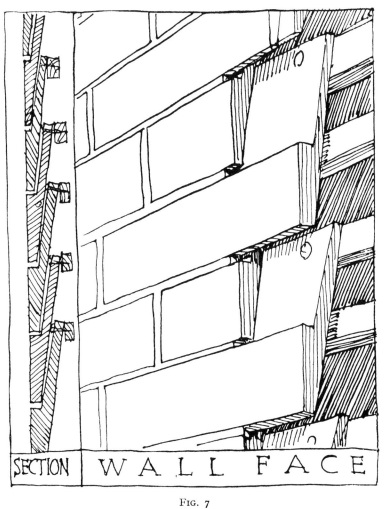

SECTION   WALL FACE

Fig. 7

grooved to give a hold for the hazel or rent oak reinforcement
of the clay daub filling.   Where these grooves exist they form
a wind and water check between timber and concrete.   But
more often the timbers are found with no such groove.   It
is then advisable to screw an oak fillet on the sides of the posts
so that when the concrete is cast in position the fillet will form
the check.   It is advisable that the fillet be screwed and not
nailed, for unless this is done it is apt to be drawn away when
slight movements occur either in the framework or the concrete.   The oak fillets may be bedded in mastic or other
waterproof bedding to make that joint water-tight.   The
concrete may be cast about half an inch back from the face
of the timbers so that it may be given a plaster finish which
will be flush with the framing face.   It is Mr. William Weir's
practice to use concrete filling in this way.

19

Wattle-and-daub

The wattle-and-daub process has recently been revived by
Mr. H. E. Forrest of Shrewsbury, and may now again be
regarded as a practical means of filling the spaces between
the timbers.   Mr. Forrest wrote a very full description of the
process for the Society for the Protection of Ancient Buildings,
and although I have not had direct experience in the use of
his methods and although some have doubts as to their success,
the matter is one of such interest as to make much of what he
wrote worth printing here.   I have, too, recently found this
method practised in Suffolk.

Mr. Forrest writes:

Durability of an oak framed building depends entirely on exposure
to sun and rain.   If protected from both, a timber building will last as
long as one constructed of stone or brick.   The north side never gets
any sunshine, and seldom any driving rain.   In almost every case
the timbers on this side will be found to be original, and still sound.
The east face suffers but little from sun or rain, as the morning sun is
seldom strong, and rain from the east is infrequent, and when it does
come it is usually a gentle drizzle with little wind.

The south face is the one that suffers far more than any other.   The
sun blazing upon it throughout the hottest part of a summer day

causes the wood to open. Then the heavy rains from the south and south-west drive into the cracks and cause the wood to rot. But still more damage is done by the rain running down the uprights of the frame to the sill, and then being drawn by capillary attraction into the mortise holes, where it rots the tenons and the posts from the bottoms upwards.

The west face suffers in the same way, only in a less degree. It suffers more than the east face because it gets more driving rain and because the westerly sun on a summer day is hotter than the morning sun.

The above considerations apply to a timber building where no precautions have been taken to protect it from rain. But the Tudor carpenter devised a method of dealing with the problem which was not only effective, but added greatly to the beauty of his houses. He made the upper storey to overhang the lower, the overhang being supported on prolongations of the floor-joists. The verges of the gables overhung in a similar way, and were faced with barge-boards, often elaborately carved. The overhang averaged two feet, but in Shrewsbury there are examples over three feet deep. This overhang protected the lower face from the sun in the hottest part of the day when it is high in the heavens, and sheltered it from all but strongly driving rain. Most of the rain dropped off into space. I have found that where the overhang was sufficiently deep, the timbers on even the south side have lasted quite as well as those on the other faces. The frames of timber buildings all belong to one or other of two types:

(1) Close-timbered frames.
(2) Square-panelled frames.

The *close-timbered frames* prevailed throughout the fifteenth and the greater part of the sixteenth century. In these houses the frame consisted of a row of upright posts reaching from floor to ceiling and mortised at top and bottom into horizontal beams. The earlier the date the larger and closer together are the posts.

The *square-panelled frame* came into general use for external walls late in Elizabethan times, but it had been used long before that for internal partitions. Side by side with this a close-timbered frame continued in use up to about 1600, but modified by the insertion of transoms between floor and ceiling levels, and by diagonal bracings at the corners.

The *filling of the spaces* in the above two types of frame was also of two types, to correspond to the needs of each:

(1) In the close-timbered frame the filling was of *laths* (not woven) attached to the *sides* of the *upright* timbers.

(2) In the square-panelled frame the filling was of woven sticks or plaited laths (wattle-work) attached to the *upper* and *under* faces of the *horizontal* timbers.

Details. (1) The sides of the uprights had a groove cut into each, reaching from top to bottom. Into these grooves pieces of split oak lath were wedged irregularly, forming a flat series, but with irregular spaces between the laths. Clay was then applied, filling up all spaces and forming a thick layer over the laths on both faces. This was left for some time to dry; when it had set quite hard and had developed cracks all over the surface, the whole was finished with a coating of thin plaster, which ran into all the crevices, and cemented the whole filling into a solid mass which was part and parcel of the framework, and quite immovable. In order to prevent the clay "dab" from falling to pieces as it dried, some binding material was always mixed with it. All over the midlands (where flax used to be grown in every garden, and where every "spinster" made her own linen) the material used was flax-stems, the waste product of flax after the outer fibre had been removed. Straw was also used, but while this, when exposed to the air nowadays falls to bits at a touch, the flax-stems are firm and tough after the lapse of centuries.

The clay used for wattle-and-daub must be well worked up with a spade until plastic, and it must be mixed with some fibrous material as described above, or with tow.

(2) A square-panel frame was filled with wattle-work made thus: Four staves of split oak were prepared about two inches longer than the height of the panel. Two were about three inches wide, the other two about half that width. These were "sprung" into holes in the top and bottom of the frame-panel, the two wider staves to right and left, narrower ones between. Hazel boughs (in the natural state, with the bark on) were woven between these staves, forming a close basket-(or wattle-) work. Sometimes plaited laths were used instead of hazel boughs. The whole was finished with clay and plaster in the same way as described above. Strictly speaking, the familiar phrase "wattle-and-daub" can only be applied to the square panel, as there is no wattle-work in the close-timbered frame. As there is much greater shrinkage in a square, than in a narrow, panel, it is more difficult to get the filling to fit tightly into the frame, especially at the sides, because these are not grooved.[1] In restoring a timber building of this type it would be advisable to groove the sides and prolong the wattles into the grooves. This would give a firm attachment to the frame on all four sides. A timber framed building treated in this way will be impervious to wind or rain. . . .

Mr. Forrest does not of necessity advocate a slavish adherence to the old methods when repairs are in progress, but strongly recommends that the old principle should be held to.

[1] I have found this done in old buildings in the way indicated on the sketch (see Fig. 8).

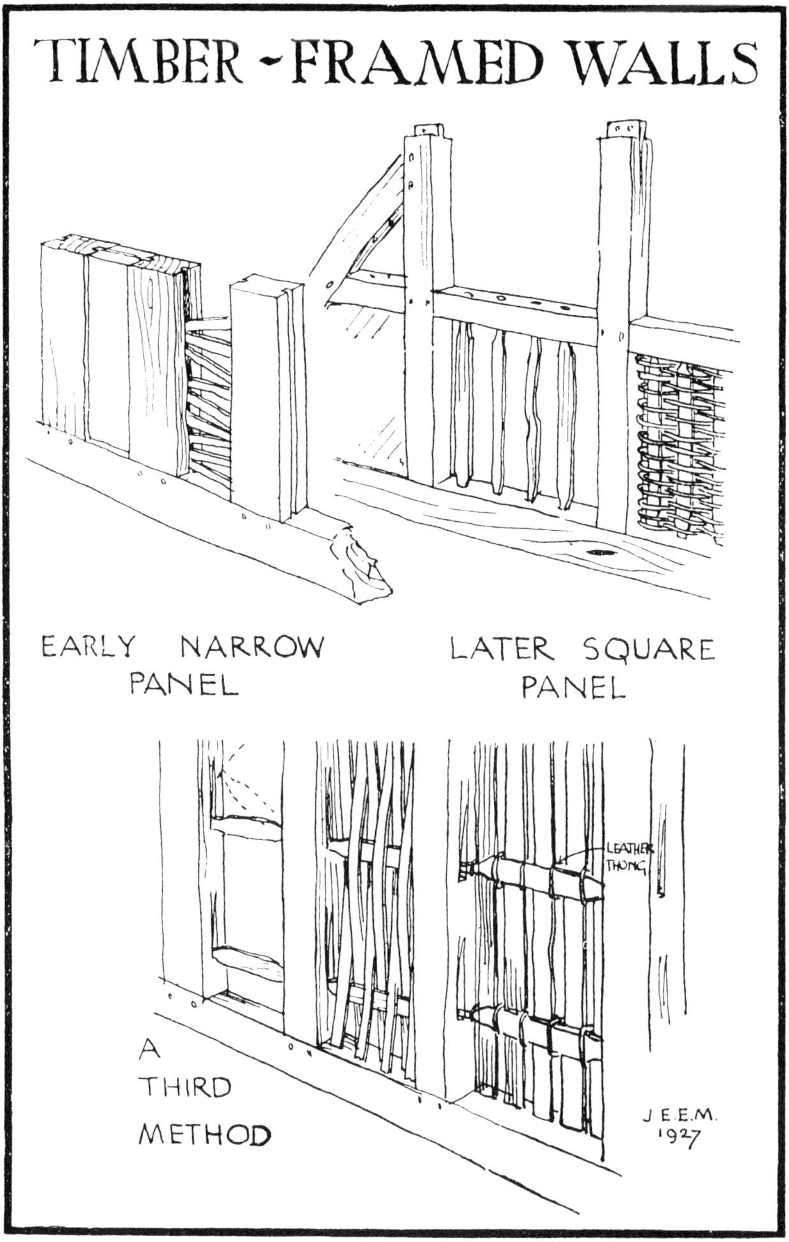

TIMBER-FRAMED WALLS

EARLY NARROW
PANEL

LATER SQUARE
PANEL

LEATHER
THONG

A
THIRD
METHOD

J.E.E.M.
1927

FIG. 8

He suggests that in close timber framing strips of slate may be used instead of laths, and in wide framing suggests metal. Probably iron is not the best metal because it is so liable to expansion due to rust. An examination of old examples of wattle-and-daub will disclose an immense variety of methods of fixing, though they all more or less accord with Mr. Forrest's description.

The Surface Treatment of the Oak of Half-timbered Houses

There is evidence that the custom of darkening the oak work in half-timber houses did not begin before the seventeenth century. In many unrestored half-timber houses the timbers are limewashed. It is difficult to say whether this finish was the original, or whether the oak was left its natural colour while the panels only were whitened. The Society for the Protection of Ancient Buildings holds that the oak should not be stained dark, that it should either be brushed down and left clean, or that it should be whitened with the panels. This opinion, I find, is confirmed by most who have experience in the treatment of these buildings.

The repair of the oak framing itself may be done as is usual in carpentry, and as is suggested in the chapter dealing with timber roofs. Where new timbers must be used they may be left from the saw or adzed. It is Mr. Weir's custom to let the saw marks show, and only to do such other work to the timber as may be necessary to secure proper joints. A number of other architects prefer that all new timbers should be finished with the adze, but as this practice seems to be derived from a desire to revive an old method of dressing timber, now little used, rather than from any practical advantage, the writer feels this tooling to be an affectation, and, therefore, considers that it should be avoided. The adze is a valuable tool but in this practice it seems much abused. It is, for instance, useful to remove sap-wood by cutting chamfers from the angles of new beams. And the removal of sap-wood from structural timbers is important, for it is there that the wood-worm usually begins its destructive work.

The repair of the oak framing of a "half-timber" building differs in one respect from that of a roof, namely, in that it is exposed to the weather. For this reason it is desirable, as far as may be, to avoid cutting tenons or other holes in the upper sides of timbers. Examination of old walls will show the joints where rot usually starts, and new joints should be designed to withstand rather than to encourage decay.

But beside the oak framed walls which were used in England until the end of the seventeenth century there are a number of later and smaller buildings, tile-hung, weather-boarded, or plastered, where pine and fir are used for the structural members. The repair of such framework may be done in the same way as is recommended for the older oak work. It has, however, been suggested that the substitution of concrete or ferro-concrete for the timbers might be a convenient, and at the same time a permanent method of repair. Such a case has come to the notice of the writer, where the timbers of a brick-nogged wall were permeated by dry rot, and where the use of concrete packed into the spaces originally occupied by the deals appeared a reasonable and lasting way to repair the faults. Indeed the use of concrete in such positions suggests a great variety of methods which might be employed in the repair of those buildings of this class which deserve to be preserved for their beauty or other desirable qualities.

THE DECAY OF MATERIALS

Surface Decay of Masonry

Surface decay of stone or brick is due to a great variety of causes. Each material differs in composition, even stones taken from the same quarry vary, and when these are subjected to conditions which again differ, and this sometimes in a single building, the complexity of the problem becomes apparent.

The agents of decay are organic, mechanical and chemical.

Organic decay is chiefly due to visible vegetable growths, but attack by bacteria is now also suspected, though it is not as yet definitely established.

Mechanical decay is caused by expansion and contraction due to changes of temperature, by frost, by wind, and windblown sand, by damage due to carelessness, or done on purpose, and by ordinary wear.

Chemical decay is principally due to the presence of sulphur gases and ammonia carried into the air by coal-smoke and deposited in the stone, brick, or mortar by rain-water.

In all cases of surface decay *cure* is at present very difficult, if not impossible, but partial or nearly complete *prevention* is possible, and should be attempted; for at the worst the causes of decay may be interrupted or hindered. In short, decay in building materials should be treated on the same principles and with the same intention as are the ailments of human beings. The life of a building is longer than that of a man, but in the end both become dust. It is for us to secure the longest possible life for that which is fine and noble, neither does this desire for the security of the old conflict with the urge to have new and gracious buildings about us.

Vegetation on Buildings

Decay in stone or brick caused by visible vegetable growth is mainly indirect. Lichens and mosses must draw some nourishment from the stone itself, and may even secrete harmful acids, but they do these things to so small an extent that their powers of damage may be ignored. Mosses, because they hold moisture, may sometimes help frost to break up stone or may aid the entrance of harmful chemical agents, but as they seldom grow on badly decaying or crumbling stone they are rather a proof of soundness than a sign that precautions should be taken. Since these small plants do little harm, and because they add colour and quality which few fail to admire, they may be preserved. In regard to this question

Mr. Noël Heaton advised the Society for the Protection of Ancient Buildings that "lichens can be removed from tombstones by spraying or brushing with a weak solution of zinc fluosilicate, which hardens the stone at the same time." But he wrote also, "the destructive effect that grey and yellow lichens usually develop is more than counterbalanced by the protection they give to the stone," and advised that these plants should be left alone except where they interfere with the legibility of inscriptions, etc.

It is the larger vegetation which is damaging, first, to the structure itself, and secondarily, to the surface materials of which the structure is built. Shrubs, young trees, and especially ivy send their roots into the joints of a wall and draw nourishment from lime mortar, causing it to break up. While the roots increase in size, disintegration accelerates, for as they grow they displace more material, rain penetrates the joints more easily, and the plant, of its own activity, increases the sustenance on which it thrives. Sometimes fine rootlets even penetrate minute crevices of the stones themselves, and as they grow exert force enough to split hard stones. Like many another cause of decay the evil which larger vegetation brings attacks the heart of a building, and with the heart destroys the surface. It is because the removal of vegetation must be begun from without, although the damage caused by its roots within must be cured when repair to the building is done, that the subject is considered here with surface decay. For although the roots must be traced and removed even from the very centre of a wall, first of all the branches of the plant must go. All growths that draw sustenance from a wall should be cut down.

The Removal of Ivy and other Creepers

Ivy, of all English plants, is most damaging, and it may best be removed in the following manner: The stems should be cut where convenient; the whole of the plant from five feet or so above the ground to the bottom of the roots should immediately be removed, and the rest should be left to wither. When the stems are dried and shrunken the remainder of the plant should be lifted from the wall. To pull it off before may disturb the surface unnecessarily. And in cutting the ivy it is well to order that saws and not axes shall be used, for with the careless use of axes carved, moulded, and other stonework may be damaged. As to those plants which root in a wall, and take no nourishment from the ground, they should at once be cut down, and when repairs are being done their roots removed. Until the building is cleared of the larger forms of vegetation all the defects cannot be seen, and the survey cannot be complete nor the necessary repairs be decided on.

Those who admire creepers on old walls may be distressed by these recommendations. They should remember that theirs is a selfish pleasure, for unless it is impossible for these plants to obtain nourishment from a wall they will send roots between the stones, and so hasten its downfall. Besides ivy and young trees I have seen damage caused by honeysuckle, by wistaria, and by Virginia creepers of all kinds. If creepers are allowed to grow at all, the joints between the stones, etc. must be impervious to moisture for their full depth, for thus it becomes impossible for these plants to get nourishment except from the ground. And it is not to walls alone that these plants do harm, for if they are neglected, and at any time that may happen, they are apt to reach the roofs, the most vulnerable parts of buildings. Therefore those who have the care of buildings which are valuable to more than themselves, either on account of beauty or age or workmanship, should see to it that there is no risk of damage from this source.

Traditional Methods for Treating Surface Decay

With the exception of physical damage, of changes due to temperature, and of wind-borne agents, the causes of most surface decay are conveyed by, and are due to, the presence of water. And this agent of decay acting in conjunction with those it carries, does its evil work by effecting actual changes in the structure of a material or by causing differences of pressure within it. The freezing of water in saturated stone, brick, or mortar is only more apparently damaging because its effects are more sudden. That water-borne solvents are the chief cause of decay may not be apparent at once when it is remembered that stones which are inaccessible to rain powder away. But, nevertheless, this is so, for within a building the products of burning gas (of which water is one) attack stone through the condensation on its surface. In a sheltered cloister mist-borne acids condense on the surfaces of vaulting and walls; and in neither case is there any chance that these active agents will be carried to the ground in a downpour of rain. Owing to the complex nature of the causes of surface decay an attempt to check it by chemical means is very difficult, and as yet it seems that only the elements of this science are understood. It appears likely also that even when chemical information on the subject is complete, the older well-tried methods which have developed with the development of building traditions will for ever be the necessary base from which to work. It is, therefore, our first object not only in these pages, but in the actual work of repair, to decide how the penetration of water may be prevented and how exposed surfaces may be made to throw it off quickly, and this by the use of traditional methods. This is the essence of all surface protection. To increase the resistance of the surfaces of affected material itself is a secondary matter, though an important one. Yet it is in discovering how this may be done that chemical knowledge can be useful; and in this work rapid development seems immediately impending.

It has already been said that the object of surface repair is to avoid renewal so that the individual qualities of an ancient building may be preserved. To obtain this end I have found it helpful to consider each stone, each brick, and each joint on a decaying surface as though it was the only one to be treated. If one sets out to preserve a stone it is not renewed, but treated individually. If one sets out to preserve a wall of stones, one is apt to suggest renewal; but a wall is made of separate stones, and if they are individually preserved the wall is preserved entire with its original and acquired character. Indeed this attitude of mind lies at the root of the preservation of ancient buildings. It is this difference which distinguishes the repairer from the commercial contractor, whether he deals with "church" or other work.

Materials available : their Merits and Demerits

It is unwise to say that any materials usually used in walling should be forbidden in repairs; any one of them may be suitable; neither is it necessarily right to use a material of the same kind as the one to be repaired. This would be otherwise if the object of the work were to "Restore" the original form and colour. That is not our object, but to hinder decay in a surface that is in danger of disappearing.

A decaying stone may be replaced by a new one, but this is seldom the best course to take. The disadvantages of using new stone are (a) less of the original work is preserved; (b) the removal of the old stone to make way for the new may loosen or damage those adjoining; (c) the new stone makes an unpleasant patch, more unpleasant because often more noticeable than that made by other materials; (d) stone is not a plastic material and cannot conveniently be modelled to conform to the irregularities of the surface on either hand; (e) a new stone cannot be so tightly set in a wall as one that was laid in position during building, and thus it may throw on to the adjoining stones a greater pressure than they can bear without fracture. Thus a new stone inserted into a worn string course will have keen edges projecting beyond those on either side, and to make the junction between it and the old less conspicuous, renewal is continued until at some place the old moulded band of stonework retains its full section. In this way more original work disappears than is necessary. New stone, then, should not necessarily be used for the repair work of stone buildings unless there is structural reason for it. And this will be readily accepted as sound advice when it is re-membered that it is seldom necessary to renew a stone (of any kind) because of surface decay alone. Complete renewal of a stone need not be made until decay is so far advanced as to cause it to be a source of structural danger. Indeed, partial renewal in any material should be undertaken only with the object of prolonging the life of what exists and is endangered, whether it be the life of the piece itself or of its neighbour. It is very rare that renewal should be made in order that the original form should be recovered.

The Use of New Stone

In cases where new stone seems to be the best material for repair it does not necessarily follow that it should come from the same quarry as the old, though it is advisable that it should be taken from a similar formation of like colour. In the selection of stone the advice of local masons, coupled with an examination of the stone buildings of the neighbourhood and a knowledge of the quarries, is indispensable.

It is held by some that stone that differs from the old should be chosen for repair works on an old building, on the ground that the future archæologist may not mistake the repair for original work. This seems to stress too far the archæological point of view and too little that of common sense.

The way in which new stone is worked is important, and on this there are many opinions. It is generally conceded that the "drag" should not be used after stones are set, just as it should never on any account be used to redress old masonry or to remove paint or dirt. And it is certain that an attempt to give "texture" to a new stone already worked fine with the drag by chiselling the face is bad practice. Medieval customs should be a guide in this matter, but as the practice varied in time and place, no standard rule can be laid down. Many architects hold any stone finished with a drag anathema, and the same men advise others to learn from medieval work what should be done. But this tool was used to some extent as early as the thirteenth century in working the deep hollow mouldings of which the masons then were fond. By the fifteenth century the drag was always used in England for dressing highly-finished freestone, when indeed this was not rubbed down smooth. But while it was used in this way in fine work the quoin stones of rubble walling were sometimes left, one might almost say, partially worked from the chisel, for in such rougher work the masons often did not trouble to cut away the stone to the full depth of the little pits left by the quarry hammer used in the preliminary squaring. My conclusion in the matter is that it is better not to trouble about obtaining textures like the old, but to follow the spirit which guided the masons of old days; that is, to do the least possible to a stone that will make it fit for its purpose in fine or coarse work, using whatever tools may be convenient and will make for economy of labour. But whilst making this statement, in agreement with others I own that I enjoy much more to see a stone that has been cut with a sharp tool than one which has been worn into shape by the toothed edge of the steel drag.

The Use of Other Materials : Brick, Tile, Mortar, and Artificial Stone

Decaying stonework may be renewed in brickwork as was often successfully done one hundred and more years ago, but in our day this is considered bad practice, being subject to the same disadvantages as the repair by stone, as well as to changes of colour and texture. But because repairs in brick are not recommended to-day it does not follow that the old repairs in this material should be removed. As a rule it is best to preserve these patches along with the original work.

Mortar made with either lime, cement, or Roman cement may be used, and if it were durable when used alone would have every advantage over either stone or brick; but since experience has shown that these materials used in bulk seldom adhere permanently to the stonework behind them, they may when used alone be ruled out as useless. In conjunction with other materials, however, they form the basis of most systems of traditional repair.

There remain three methods to be considered, and all three are to be recommended on occasion. All three can be used with the minimum of disturbance to old work. These methods may be likened to those used by a dentist when he lengthens the life of a decaying tooth. In both cases the object and the means taken to secure it are similar. In both cases the decayed portions are drilled or cut away, and the sound material is only cut at all to obtain a key for the stopping, and in both cases the object is to preserve original material. Also in both works the material selected is chosen

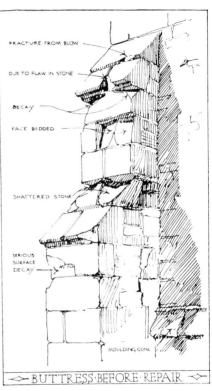

FRACTURE FROM BLOW

DUE TO FLAW IN STONE

DECAY

FACE BEDDED

SHATTERED STONE

SERIOUS SURFACE DECAY

MOULDING GONE

BUTTRESS·BEFORE·REPAIR

Fig. 9

because of its plastic nature, for its durability, for its adhesive qualities, and to some extent on account of appearances.

The method which up till now has been used with most success is that which Mr. William Weir has perfected, namely, repair with pieces of tile laid flat in mortar and keyed to the sound core of the stonework. A diagram and photographs are reproduced to illustrate this method (see Figs. 9–16).

The material is very durable, the surface is plastic and can be modelled to fit adjoining stones, it is so keyed to the stone backing as to become a part of it, and the finished texture and colour are not objectionable, and "weather" pleasantly. The work can be done by any intelligent bricklayer or walling-mason, though until the system is properly understood by him supervision must be very close indeed. The composition of the mortar used is most important, and is considered with the question of pointing. For key to the sound stone Mr. Weir relies on chases cut to the width of a tile and into these every third or fourth piece of tile or every third or fourth course is set. An ingenious trades-man will so arrange these chases and dowel holes that the tilework cannot come away from the stone except it be fractured. When completed the tiled work is usually best plastered over, though it is sometimes left show-ing with the joints filled flush (see Fig. 16, Ratcliffe-on-Soar Church).

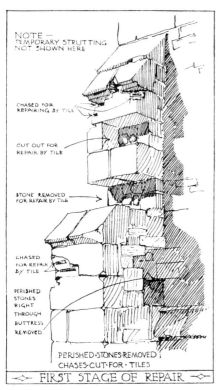

NOTE —
TEMPORARY STRUTTING
NOT SHOWN HERE

CHASED FOR
REPAIRING BY TILE

CUT OUT FOR
REPAIR BY TILE

STONE REMOVED
FOR REPAIR BY TILE

CHASED
FOR REPAIR
BY TILE

PERISHED
STONES
RIGHT
THROUGH
BUTTRESS
REMOVED

PERISHED·STONES·REMOVED
CHASES·CUT·FOR · TILES

—◇— FIRST STAGE OF REPAIR —◇—

FIG. 10

The second method is something similar, but the stopping material is fine concrete. Mr. C. C. Thompson has developed this treatment in the repair work he has done, though he also uses tile. It is more difficult to get a permanent key for

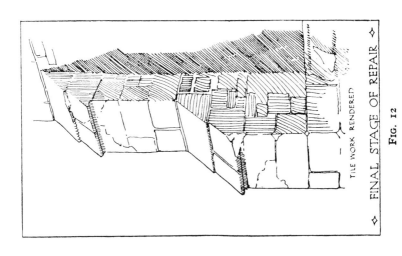

TILE WORK RENDERED

✧ FINAL STAGE OF REPAIR ✧

Fig. 12

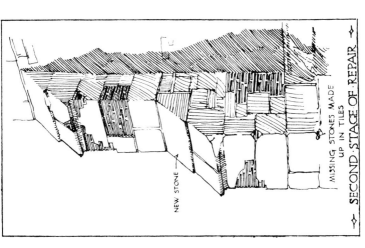

NEW STONE

MISSING STONES MADE
UP IN TILES

✧ SECOND STAGE OF REPAIR ✧

Fig. 11

concrete than for tile, and it is more difficult to keep the material in position when it is first applied.   Stout copper wire bent to suit the occasion, and with its ends well set into holes specially drilled for them, materially strengthens the connection between new and old, and will also reinforce the concrete. Copper wire can be used for similar purposes in conjunction with repair by tile.   Again the success of the work depends on the composition of the concrete and on supervision.

The third method has not yet been used to the greatest advantage, neither has it yet been fully proved by experience that it will stand the test of time.   It consists in using compositions known in the building trade as "synthetic stone." These are proprietary articles devised to restore decayed stonework to its original form at less cost than is incurred by renewal.   And at the outset it should be said that no proprietary article should be allowed in the repair of ancient work unless all its ingredients and the manner of preparation are made known.   Usually the firms selling these "stones" insist that their men shall be employed, and these men are accustomed to regard the material as a means for the reproduction of the old forms, making "reproductions" which more often than not have an unpleasant mechanical appearance. The men employed are not as a rule trained to preserve, but to reproduce, and, therefore, their work commonly results in the loss of remaining features which it should be their object to preserve.   "Synthetic stone" is applied like mortar; it is a plastic material.   There is reason to believe that under the supervision of men who thoroughly understand what the object of repair is, such patent materials would be useful. They should be thought of as a mortar that has exceptional adhesive qualities and which sets very hard, and which is likely to resist the attacks of an acid-laden atmosphere.   They weather differently from stone or mortar, drying out after a wet spell more quickly than either of these, and thus for a time are more conspicuous, which is a disadvantage.   The base of these materials is usually stone-dust which gives the finished work a much closer texture than is desirable.   It is therefore suggested

FIG. 13. LIMPSFIELD CHURCH, SURREY.
A WINDOW IN THE NORTH WALL
BEFORE REPAIR

Fig. 15. Limpsfield Church, Surrey. A Window in the North Wall After Repair in 1927

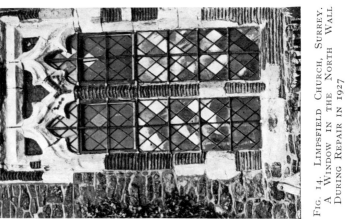

Fig. 14. Limpsfield Church, Surrey. A Window in the North Wall During Repair in 1927

that a quantity of coarse sand should be added to the mixture, for this would certainly improve its appearance.   21

In finishing the mortar joints between the dressed stone it is well to follow the example of the original builders, who usually left them flush with the face. Care should be taken not to spread the mortar beyond the joints over the stonework, and feather-edges of mortar should not be allowed. It is good practice to finish the surface of the mortar joints with a soft dry brush, for this closes any crevices left by the trowel.

Photographs are reproduced here to illustrate these recommendations. Some speak for themselves; some need further explanation.

In the photograph taken in 1914 of the doorway into the transept of Chester Cathedral (see Fig. 17) it will be seen that decay was serious. Repair by stone was the method chosen, with the result that for genuine medieval work we now have a modern study in Gothic architecture (Fig. 18), a change that is to be regretted. It was a case eminently suited for repair by tile and mortar stopping; the decayed joints could have been treated as were those to be seen in other photographs reproduced here. This work may be contrasted with the repair of the wall base done at Ratcliffe-on-Soar Church (see Fig. 16).

The three photographs—before, during, and after the repair—of a window at Limpsfield Church (Figs. 13, 14, and 15) show that more of the original stone was saved by this method than would have been the case had the outer face of the mullion and tracery been renewed in stone. This work was finished in 1928 by Mr. E. Bowden.

The photograph of the south aisle of Henley-in-Arden Church (see frontispiece), taken after the work had been done for some years, gives a better idea of the final appearance of the tile method of repair than does that of the Limpsfield window, taken immediately on completion.

Two materials difficult to remove from old stone and brickwork are paint and the hardened accumulation of sooty deposit; it is occasionally desirable to remove the first, and often the second.

The Removal of Paint from Masonry, etc.

22   As a protective, paint is excellent; but it is sometimes dis-figuring. In a number of cases no attempt should be made to remove paint, and an instance of this will be found in the wonderful sedilia and piscina of Tilty Church, Essex. Where the sooty deposit hangs it is disfiguring, but it appears likely that it most accumulates at those points where decay has not begun or is very slow.

Paint may be removed by using paint remover made from such solvents as acetone. These do not affect the stone itself, but after their use all traces of the ingredients must be washed from the stone with water containing a solution which has a natural affinity for them; finally, the stonework must be thoroughly washed down with clean water. Preparations containing caustic soda (and many proprietary "removers" contain it) should on no account be used. The prescription given in Rivington contains caustic soda and is therefore to be avoided. Some advise the use of quicklime for removing paint from stone.

An acetone "remover" is also useful in getting rid of the hardened sooty deposit, but it is sometimes difficult to shift this by these means alone. When the York water gate was repaired by the London County Council some years ago a steam jet was used to free the stone from this matter, and the stone does not appear to have suffered from the treatment. The steam jet, however, should not be used till it has been ascertained by experiment that it will not, at the same time that it cleans, remove weather-resisting qualities from the surface of the stone. Mr. Arthur R. Warnes, in his book *Building Stones*, gives much useful information on the subject of removing dirt, and his conclusion is that the steam jet does no harm.

Surface Decay of Brickwork

Sound brickwork is better able to resist the agents of decay than stone. Only under-fired or badly-made bricks suffer

Fig. 16.   Ratcliffe - on - Soar   Church,
Leicestershire.   Repairs   at   the
West End of the South Aisle

FIG. 17. CHESTER CATHEDRAL. SURFACE DECAY DUE TO NEGLECT, BUT
STILL REPARABLE, 1914

from these agents, and in fine old buildings there are but few of them. Where decay exists it is usually in single bricks, and not in stretches of the wall surface, and in such cases the faulty bricks should be cut out and replaced by new. If old bricks can be obtained from the core of a wall during repairs, necessarily done to it, they may be used on the surface to replace missing bricks there. Otherwise new bricks, which have been made in the same way as the old and of the same size, should be used. Although it is not quite in accordance with the object of this book to refer to the method of shaping bricks in use in parts of England before the sixteenth century, and to some extent during that century, yet as this method is little known, and is of interest to those who value ancient buildings, it is here described. From an examination of such bricks the following deductions have been made: A piece of land was levelled and rammed. On this was laid a layer of grass, hay, or straw, and on that again a layer of prepared brick clay. The layer of clay was rammed to the required thickness; but an examination of old walls built from such bricks show that an even thickness was not always maintained. This layer was then cut to the size desired for the bricks. The earlier bricks, those of the fourteenth century, are quite often not much less than a foot by half a foot. Now this size is not much different from half the size of the bricks most commonly used by the Romans in Britain. As time passed the size of the bricks was decreased. I have been told, but I do not remember by whom, that the Romans used the same method of brick-making. It may be yet found that the art of brick-making never entirely disappeared from England after their time. Bricks made in this way retain on one side the marks of the grass and hay, and on the other the surface is often raised a little at the edges by the withdrawal of the tool with which they were cut.

It is commonly said that such buildings as the ruined Church of St. Pancras at Canterbury and the Cathedral at St. Albans are built of re-used Roman bricks. This may be so. But I have never heard that the mortar in which they are laid has been examined to make sure that traces of Roman mortar still adhere to these bricks, as would surely be the case had the bricks been re-used. If no Roman mortar is to be found I should accept this as a proof that the bricks were made when the buildings were put up. I have examined the surfaces of St. Pancras Church carefully, also a few pieces of loose brick near it. I could find only one kind of mortar.[1]

Brickwork seldom perishes over large areas of a wall, but instances do occur, as at Kirby Muxloe near Leicester. There the surface within about three feet of the water-level of the moat had disappeared. In this case the walls were amply thick enough to be structurally sound without refacing, and the joints were cleaned out and refilled and repointed. The work was well and successfully done by His Majesty's Office of Works during the time when Sir Frank Baines was director of works. In the same building there were elsewhere patches of brickwork where the facing, although it had not fallen, was loose and away from the heart of the wall. Here each brick was separately repaired by sticking the broken piece on to the sound. I have not inquired what medium was used for this purpose.

Single bricks may also be lastingly and agreeably repaired with well-prepared mortar.

It seems to have been the mediaeval custom in England to cover brickwork with plaster. Whether this was done because the builders did not trust the weather-resisting qualities of brick, or because they felt it was a base material for a monumental building, is not known. Where original plaster remains it should be repaired and maintained. Where it has been removed it may be well to leave the brick showing. When the bricks were left exposed, the mortar joints were carefully finished. A great variety of joints were used, but they were seldom flush. In the repair of a building it is well in each case to follow the example of the old builders in this matter. If for some reason the mortar chosen for the new

[1] As to the bricks used at St. Pancras, I could see nothing to show that they were not made as suggested above, and little to indicate that they were.

joint cannot be modelled as was the old, it is then usually
advisable to point flush as is suggested for masonry joint. 23

The gate-house of Trinity College, Cambridge, is an example
of a building where no brickwork was allowed to show when
it was built. Later in its history the stone as well as the
intervening plastered surfaces were covered with plaster.
Recently both the late and the original plaster have been
removed. Only a small patch of the original plastered brickwork remains, and that in an imperfect condition. The plain
walling of the great church of Walpole St. Peter is also of brick,
but it retains its original plaster in good condition. Other
brick-built churches in the same district show traces of old
plaster.

Where old brickwork has been plastered at a later date
the plaster should not of necessity be removed. An attempt
to discover the reason which led to the application of plaster
should be made before a decision is reached as to this. It may
be the bricks were porous and the removal of the plaster
would again allow the walls to become damp.

Flint and Stone Rubble Surfaces

Flint is imperishable and a wall surface of this material only
decays when the mortar joints perish. The repair of a flint
wall is more a matter of pointing than of renewal of the flints
themselves. The flints used may be found to be knapped,
partly knapped, or as they were quarried. In a properly
knapped flint wall the joints are so fine that they hardly
show; and in rubble walls the medieval pointing was very
full, almost or quite amounting to plaster. In almost every
flint building patches of the original surface may be found,
either under the eaves or in some other well-protected place.
In repair of the pointing, or as it may be called, the mortar
filling, the original fullness should be reproduced in sound
mortar; and in buildings erected in the medieval tradition,
the joints between individual flints should not be pressed
back. When such rough flint work is to be repaired in patches

only, it may be well to vary this rule in order that the new patches may not contrast too strongly with the adjoining and partly-worn face. As a rule, however, very full pointing, almost amounting to plaster, finished with a soft brush, is the practice generally to be recommended. The sparkle of weather-worn flint walling may, to some extent, be obtained on new work by cleaning the exposed pieces of flint of all traces of mortar or lime.

The surface of stone rubble walling is usually best treated in the same way as rubble flint walls.

External Plaster on Masonry, etc.

It is, however, often difficult to decide how to treat plaster which has been applied to the outside of an old wall, sometimes centuries after it was built. It is common to find mediaeval rubble walls which have received in the seventeenth century or later a thick coat of lime and hair plaster roughcasted. To tear off the later plaster is by no means always the best course to take; it may be better to repair it. As in the case of plaster-covered brick, the reason why the plaster was put on should be discovered. It may be that it was done to keep rain from driving through the wall, or it may be that the old surface was shabby. Mr. William Weir is of opinion that it was often done because it was less trouble to replaster than to repoint. In deciding this, reference to walls in the district built of like materials is a guide. If it is found that it is the practice to plaster or rough-cast similar walls, it will be with considerable risk that different treatment is adopted. If similar walls without external plaster are common, the condition of the later plaster will probably be the deciding factor. To some extent the condition of the wall face below will indicate what should be done; whether it can be made easily weather-resisting, and whether it has suffered much or been disfigured before or when the plaster was put on. As a rule, if there is a prospect that this later plaster will last a fair number of years, it is best repaired. If it has become very loose and

FIG. 18. CHESTER CATHEDRAL.   SURFACE RENEWAL INSTEAD OF SURFACE
REPAIR

FIG. 19. A Good Rough-cast Surface and the Quoin of a Rubble-built Wall
from a Cottage at Castle Combe

has been much patched, it had better be removed. When removed, the original wall face should be treated as though the later plaster had never been put on. Like stonework, plaster was usually limewashed, and a repetition of this process will make it more durable and also, when repairs have been done, will hide the patches.

When decaying or loose plaster is being treated it will sometimes be found well to treat sections of the wall face only; thus the surface between buttresses or below or above a string course can be conveniently stripped or repaired independently of other parts.

With regard to replastering old walls, the same precautions should be taken and preparations made as for repointing; but in addition no mosses or lichens should be left on the stone surface, for plaster will not set on to stone, brick, or mortar that is not absolutely clean. Indeed this is the reason why much of the later plaster is found to be loose. Under proper supervision, a wire brush might be useful in this preparatory cleaning.

In dealing with medieval buildings new plaster should be laid on rather thinly in one-coat work to follow the irregularities of the wall face. It may be laid on with a wooden or steel trowel and finished as recommended for mortar joints with a soft dry brush. On no account should screeds be used. When rough cast is used the pebbles should be finer than is now the custom for modern domestic work, and the surface should receive three coats of limewash. The accompanying illustration (Fig. 19) of a cottage wall so treated shows such a surface very well done. 24

The junction of plaster with dressed quoin stones was often managed badly in restorations of the nineteenth century. An examination of rubble-built walls shows that the quoins were often set rather full so that the mortar or thin plaster surface of the finished wall could stop against them. Alternatively, sometimes the quoin stones were in the same plane as the more projecting stones of the rubble-work, and the plaster was skimmed more thinly till it died out on the quoin stones.

In both cases plaster and quoin stones were originally lime-washed together. One or other of these practices should be adhered to. The later lime and hair plaster was much thicker and was as a rule taken over these quoin stones, and where it is to be retained and repaired it is better to follow the later practice than to attempt to expose the quoin stones by stopping the plaster short of them, leaving it projecting an inch or three-quarters of an inch in front of the stone face.

25   It is seldom or never desirable to repeat modelled or patterned plaster work when repairs are being done.

In medieval work external plaster on stone or brick walls was in the nature of mortar spread over the wall face. I do not remember finding hair used in such plaster. This material seems to have been used to prevent later plaster falling away from walls which were not sufficiently cleaned or prepared. For new plaster work to this kind of walling, mortar as used for pointing is recommended. To secure complete setting, in new plaster, it should be watched and sheltered as recommended for pointing.

Damp-proofing Plaster Work

I do not propose to describe the proprietary waterproofing liquids and powders which may be used in mortar, plaster, or, for that matter, in concrete, to prevent the ingress of either ground damp or driven rain. For concrete an admixture of heavy mineral oil has been recommended in the following proportions—eight per cent by weight of oil to a measure of cement. But where this is used, it is said, there should be a

26   slight increase of cement in proportion to the aggregate.

Internal Plaster

The medieval builder never left the inside of a building which had rubble or rough stone walls without plaster unless it was the commonest sort of farm building. In repairing medieval buildings, therefore, the same practice is recom-

mended. It was also the medieval practice to decorate
plaster and stonework with colour and wall pictures. Such
pictures are found on the plaster direct and on limewash.
It is therefore surely unwise to disturb any internal medieval
plaster work that remains. When these walls have already
been stripped of plaster, the first opportunity should be taken
to cover them again.

Pointing and Mortar Joints

In considering whether old mortar joints between the stones,
etc. of which the wall is built should be remade, that is, whether
pointing should be done, two questions should be asked. Is
the existing condition such as is likely to hasten the decay of
the surface material or to allow rain to enter the heart of the
wall? And what was the original surface of the mortar joints
like? If the existing joints are such as will allow rain to
penetrate or lie in them, they should be remade; other joints
should not be touched. Having settled that repointing is
necessary, the form of the new joint should be agreed on,
having regard to what the original joint was like.

Before pointing is begun the joints to be so treated should
be raked out at least twice as deeply as the thickness of the
joint, and the sides, etc. of the stones which will come in contact with the new joint should be cleaned of all old mortar
and dirt. The cleaning of the joints should only be entrusted
to men who appreciate the value of the keen arrises or edges
of stone or brick, for without great care damage may happen
to them. The joint so prepared should be thoroughly wet
before, and at the time when, the new mortar is put in.   27

Mortar

As to mortar for pointing old buildings. The ordinary
rules in use on new work apply; but seeing that the building
to be treated is valuable because of its age and other
characteristics, greater care should be taken to get the best
ingredients and to mix them in the most suitable proportions.

Lime mortar is often successfully used and is to be preferred if complete setting can be assured, because it was used in the original building. But lime mortar cannot always be relied on for pointing old walls, because even when sheltered and watered during the first weeks of setting, the body of a joint will sometimes dry out and become powdery behind a well-hardened face. To make certain of success trials should be made in situations like those where the mortar is to be used, and these should be narrowly inspected before approval, to ensure that the suggested mortar possesses those qualities which are desired. It is well that mortar when it is set should not be harder than the stone about it.

Hydraulic lias limes, ground to fine powder, are commonly used for mortar for pointing old walls. Mortar made with these limes must be used with caution, because it requires to be constantly damp, if "setting" is to be complete throughout. It is suitable when the mass of the wall is still wet after building operations, for then the walls themselves will provide the moisture needed by the pointing mortar to set it hard.

No better mortar for pointing is made than that used by the Ancient Monuments department of His Majesty's Office of Works and it is of this kind, made from finely-ground hydraulic lime mixed with three parts of clean sharp and coarse sand. But it is the practice of this department to clean out the joints between the stones to a very great depth, and to fill these to within two or three inches of the face with cement mortar tamped home; thus the walls contain enough moisture to ensure that the surface mortar does not dry before hardening is complete.

To avoid any risk of pointing mortar drying out before it hardens, a mortar that sets quickly, that is, before it can dry, may be used. For this reason Mr. William Weir uses cement-made mortar for pointing, but he uses less cement in proportion to sand than is the common practice. The exact proportions of the mortar depend on the quality of the sand and its position in use.

And with regard to cement mortar, the common report that

it contains ingredients which start decay in stone is stated by Mr. Arthur R. Warnes in his book on *Building Stones* to be unsound; for he points out that if anything lime contains more harmful properties than cement. Since no building can be done without mortar of one or other kind, and since experience shows that the results are good in both cases, this point may be ignored. A disadvantage of cement mortar is the efflorescence that sometimes appears near the joints in which it has been used.

The Society for the Protection of Ancient Buildings is accustomed as a general rule to recommend a mortar described below; this it does because the mortar is known to be safe and to set well, though intimate knowledge of the special circumstances of each case, not always available at a distance, might well show other mortars to be more suitable. The Society recommends that six or seven parts of coarse sharp clean sand be mixed with one part of lime, ground, slaked, or hydrated, beaten up with water at the same time. This may be left to stand, being kept moist. When it is wanted it may be used in the following way: Six or seven parts of the mixture may be taken and "knocked up" with one part of ordinary Portland cement, the whole being thoroughly incorporated. This makes a mortar that may be relied on, and one which has an agreeable colour. 28

The proportions for this mortar are chosen for these reasons: Cement mortar as ordinarily used contains too much cement; this causes it to crack and gives it an unpleasant colour. If made with too little cement, although it will set well, it is difficult to handle, as it is "short" off the trowel, and is apt to "weep" from the joints. The addition of a little lime "fattens" the mortar, that is, it makes it easy to handle, and also improves the colour.

The London County Council uses a mortar made in the following proportions: sand, eight parts; hydrated lime, one and a half parts, and Portland cement, one part.

Mortar made from cement and sand in proportions of one and three or one and four is to be avoided for surface pointing, because its colour is unpleasant, and because it is apt to crack, and these are the proportions commonly used by builders when left to themselves because of the belief that the more the cement the better the mortar.

Some advise the use of "white cement" as certain brands of Portland cement are very dark, or a proportion of it instead of ordinary cement.

But no mortar can be good unless the sand has the right qualities. Clean, sharp and coarse sand is always good for mortar, and most other sands are not. There may be local reasons, however, why other sands are more convenient, and when this is so they should be tested before use by actual trial in conditions similar to those existing where they will be. Local custom is not an infallible guide in this matter though it deserves consideration. From an examination of existing work done with such sand useful information may be had.

Professor Lethaby recommends the admixture of crushed tile with the chosen sand and Mr. Thackeray Turner advises this or crushed brick, if the latter is well fired and suitable. A proportion of either is undoubtedly useful; being of a porous nature it will absorb water, a fact which materially helps in the setting of the mortar.

Again, Mr. Thackeray Turner, following an old custom, recommends the addition of sugar to lime mortars when they are used in seasons liable to frost, to prevent the damage that follows freezing. Two pounds of commercial sugar diluted in water and mixed with each yard of mortar is the proportion he recommends.

But however carefully the ingredients of mortar are chosen, and however well mixed they may be, the success of the work also depends on their use. Great care must be taken to see that the joints are closely packed with mortar, and to make sure that the surfaces are well closed down and that no hair cracks appear. Much pointing fails because these precautions are not taken, and because the joints, before the new mortar is put in, are not raked out deeply enough nor for their full thickness throughout the ordered depth.

When joints are thick they are usually found to contain "spalls" or flakes of stone and sometimes oyster-shells. To clear the joint preparatory to pointing it may be necessary to remove these. Similar small pieces should be pressed into the mortar when re-pointing is done so that the original character may be maintained; at the same time in a thick

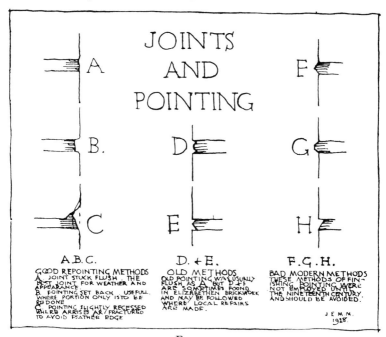

JOINTS
AND
POINTING

A.B.C.
GOOD REPOINTING METHODS
A. JOINT STUCK FLUSH — THE
BEST JOINT FOR WEATHER AND
APPEARANCE
B. POINTING SET BACK — USEFULL
WHERE PORTION ONLY IS TO BE
RE DONE
C. POINTING SLIGHTLY RECESSED
WHERE ARRIS IS AT / FRACTURED
TO AVOID FEATHER EDGE

D. + E.
OLD METHODS
OLD POINTING WAS USUALLY
FLUSH AS A. BUT D + E
ARE SOMETIMES FOUND
IN ELIZABETHEN BRICKWORK
AND MAY BE FOLLOWED
WHERE LOCAL REPAIRS
ARE MADE.

F.G.H.
BAD MODERN METHODS
THESE METHODS OF FIN-
ISHING POINTING WERE
NOT EMPLOYED UNTIL
THE NINETEENTH CENTURY.
AND SHOULD BE AVOIDED.

J E M M.
1928.

FIG. 20

joint they assist the setting of mortar and keep it stiff during that process. In some parts of the country, for instance, in that part of Surrey where Bargate stone is used, this practice of pressing small stones into the surface of a mortar joint has become a decorative feature and is known as garneting, small pieces of dark ironstone being used for the purpose. Where this practice is found to exist it should be continued.

The surfaces of mortar joints in masonry have been given a variety of forms in the past hundred years. Sometimes the

29

joint has been pressed back from the surface in a plane parallel
to it, sometimes made to project, commonly having an inverted
V section, or it has been cut back at the top and at the bottom
(see D and E, Fig. 20).   None of these fanciful finishes are to
be recommended on old walls.   Putney Church Tower, Fig. 21,
was pointed in this disagreeable way.   The sanest finish for a
joint is flush, or as nearly flush as is possible without spreading
thin films of mortar over the irregularities in the stones.   A
photograph of repairs at Ratcliffe-on-Soar shows a finish that
is satisfactory (see Fig. 16.)

Though the mortar used by the Ancient Monuments department of His Majesty's Office of Works is unsurpassed, the
author holds that the surface texture of their joints is too
even, and also sometimes too far recessed from the wall
surface.

A well-trowelled finish also has disadvantages; it tends to
bring an excess of lime or cement to the surface, which is apt
to cause hair cracks, and sometimes encourages the very surface to flake.   A good way of finishing a joint that has been
well filled with mortar pressed home is to lightly trowel it, and,
when setting has begun, to draw over the surface a soft dry
brush.   This not only gives a joint that is pleasant in appearance, but also closes the crevices, a very important matter.

Pointing must be watched during setting, and slight fractures
due to shrinkage that may occur cut out and remade.   In
dry weather fresh pointing should be kept moist.   It should
be sheltered from the sun and wind.   In cold weather protection from frost should be provided.

The custom of darkening mortar to make it "in keeping"
with adjoining weathered work is contrary to medieval
practice, and, therefore, in reality is altogether "out of keeping" with buildings of that tradition.   Further, where this
is done, though it may give a colour more like that of the old
work immediately on completion, in a few years it will be seen
to have robbed an old building of its lively brilliancy, for such
darkened mortar can never give the variety of light and dark
which is part of the characteristic beauty of an old building.

Illustrations (see Fig. 21) are given to show mortar joints both good and bad.

Cleaning and Applied Preservatives.

It has been noticed again and again that those parts of a building which are kept clean by handling or by the rubs of people passing do not decay. From this it may be concluded that regular cleaning is most desirable. Whenever building operations are in progress no opportunity should be missed to clean such parts as may usually be inaccessible or out of sight. 31

Limewash as a Good Preservative

An inspection of those buildings where the medieval practice of limewashing all stonework has been continued until to-day, will show that there no decay has occurred. This practice has been dropped almost everywhere, with the exception of old country cottages, farm buildings, and small houses; but it is now being revived. It is clear, however, from an examination of medieval stonework that it was customarily limewashed; when blocked windows are opened, when early moulded stones, found built into later walls, are examined, traces of lime are seldom wanting. The whole of the inside of King's College Chapel still retains much of its limewash; traces can be seen on the outside of the western tower of Ely; and at Cleeve Abbey in Somerset no exposed stonework, dressed or rubble, is without traces of limewash. As the buildings at Cleeve have remained more or less ruinous since the dissolution of the monasteries, there can be no doubt that the limewash is not of later date. Instances need not be multiplied. References to the cost of limewashing are found in medieval building accounts. It is established that this was the traditional custom. And where the custom has prevailed until to-day it can be seen that limewash materially helps to check decay. It is therefore recommended that, where a preservative is needed, limewash be applied to stonework after surface repair is complete; and with this in view, a leaflet recently prepared by Mr. E. E. Lofting, assistant surveyor to Westminster Abbey under Professor Lethaby, is reprinted here. This leaflet was approved by the Society for the Protection of Ancient Buildings.

32

LIMEWASH AS A STONE PRESERVATIVE

ISSUED BY THE COMMITTEE OF THE SOCIETY FOR THE PROTECTION OF ANCIENT BUILDINGS

The following notes are written as a description of a limewash which has been found generally successful as a stone preservative. The lime used for making limewash must be stone lime, and not either chalk or gas lime. It must be freshly burnt and in the lump. The particular lime described here, namely Wakeley lime, was chosen on this account, and because it is a light stone colour, and so saves in many cases the need for any colouring ingredients which may reduce the penetrative and preserving qualities of the wash. It is recommended that any question of colour or toning down should be left until after the final coat of limewash when it can easily be done (if it must be) by rubbing or brushing on a little dry colour or dust.

Wakeley lime is obtained from Messrs. G. F. Rippon and Co., lime merchants, Queen Street, Peterborough, who will send any small quantity by rail. And it is well to mention, when ordering, that fresh lumps are required as being more fiery for limewash. To mix the smallest quantity, take, for instance, an ordinary iron three gallon domestic pail. Put a lump or two of the dry lime weighing 2 lb. (rather less than more) into the pail with a quarter of a pound of crushed common salt, and quarter fill the bucket with boiling water (three quarts). So soon as the water has broken down the lumps, it will boil furiously for about a minute. Add a little more water and give it a good stir—leave it a few minutes to finish slaking—and then fill the bucket with boiling water, making twelve quarts in all. It will be seen that this pailful of limewash ready for use is about as thin as skimmed milk. The use of boiling water for slaking an already fiery lime is to set up an extra heat which produces a more completely dissolved and penetrative wash. If the lime does not boil in the pail, throw it away and try another 2 lb. lump.

After first brushing down the stonework, apply the limewash with the ordinary grass brush, lightly and patiently rubbing it into the stone. Some stones will absorb a great quantity. It is very important, especially with the first coat, to keep on saturating the stonework with the limewash, carefully working it over and over again into all the interstices. When the first coat is dry, apply a second coat—and then a third. The importance of care in the application cannot be too strongly insisted on; to do it really well requires time, patience, skill and hard work. The stonework should be normally dry—because it is then absorbent; but in very hot weather and in a hot sun it will be found that there is too much evaporation outwards to enable good work to be done.

A word on the preparation of ancient crumbling stonework for lime-washing may be useful. All attempts to fix and solidify loose scaling and sandy deposit in position, as some chemical methods try to do by spraying, seem in the end only to increase the disease; and similarly there does not appear to be much use in spraying limewash on to crumbling stone. But provided the limewash is applied with a brush and sufficiently thin, as above described, it is better to do without any preparation than to risk removing by too much brushing anything that might be saved. The problem is to find out by experiment in each case how far it is really necessary to go in the way of brushing down, because some crumbling surfaces, which work up a kind of lather as the first coat is applied, are quite hard by the time they are dry and ready for the second coat. A good method, after brushing off the surface dust and deposit, is to rub the stonework down gently with the hand or a piece of rag; this generally brings away all that need be removed, and, so far as words are concerned, may, perhaps, be safely laid down as a limit of preparation.

When all the words have been said about any particular limewash, it must be remembered that it takes some time to become a really good limewasher, and many men cannot be got sufficiently interested to take so simple a thing seriously. But carefully done, limewash is more than a protective coating on the stone—it is absorbed into and hardens the stone, and cannot be removed. Too much must not be expected from the first application to badly crumbling surfaces, for the scaling may to some extent continue. A second coating after an interval of some years, and even a third, will carry the healing process further every time.

The effect of the treatment on doing it for the first time, and a large quantity at once, may be thought startling; but experience shows that "toning down" very quickly takes place, and the old textures and irregularities quickly strike through.

But Mr. Warnes, whose valuable book on *Building Stones* has already been referred to, dismisses limewash as unscientific and disfiguring, and other chemists who have studied the question lean to his opinion if they do not actually share it. I do not doubt their knowledge but am puzzled to reconcile their opinion with the facts as they may be seen by ordinary men. Perhaps the word "unscientific" should be taken to mean "chemically unsound." In the face of this I leave it to others to explain why this preservative is in fact effective. I suggest that because limewash closes the open crevices of the surface, as on a larger scale a well-made mortar joint fills the spaces between the stones themselves, it hinders the entry of the moisture which carries the agents of decay to the stone, and so shields it from attack. I advise any who share the chemists' doubts to visit Westminster Abbey and examine the masonry of Henry the Seventh's Chapel, or the cloister walls, both newly limewashed. There are many other modern examples 36 of this craft.

It must be remembered, however, that limewash, like mortar, will only adhere to clean stones. This does not of necessity mean that all lichens should be removed before it is applied. The wash is sometimes laid over these growths as well as on the naked stonework, for where lichens are the stone is sound and needs no protection, and so it does not matter if the wash does peel off there, as it will quickly do. At other times only those stones which are decaying or which show incipient signs of decay are treated.

Mr. Weir's practice differs a little from that recommended in the sheet reprinted above. He does not recommend the addition of salt and he adds enough water to bring the wash to a very fine consistency indeed. He applies the wash in as many as five or six coats, and even then the surface as he leaves it has so little limewash on it that the coating is thinner than what is usually left after a single application by others, and also than that usually found on medieval masonry.

Mr. Warnes and some others hold that the change of colour resulting from the limewash is a disadvantage, and this no doubt it sometimes is, and on that account it is not always recommended. Yet in regard to this matter the change from one colour to another can be nothing else than the change from one beauty to another. Besides which the change is only temporary as the limewash weathers soon if it is not put on thickly. And further, limewash may be toned if desired, though the lime Mr. Lofting recommends has of itself a fair transparent colour, as though it were lightly stained with ochre and raw umber. It must be remembered also that if limewash is properly applied the texture of a building remains unaltered. Stone walls so treated cannot be mistaken for anything but stone, brickwork clearly shows, and plaster-surfaces retain the quality which makes them pleasant.

Chemical Preservatives

It has already been said that surface decay in stone is caused by so great a variety of conditions as to make it impossible to find any single preservative that can always be relied on. For this reason no proprietary preservative, hardener, or waterproofing liquid should be used unless its ingredients are known, and unless the stone to be treated has been analysed by a competent chemist experienced in the subject. I have myself seen stone that has been treated under presumably trained advice in a worse condition some seven or ten years after treatment than before. The author of *Building Stones* confirms this in his book. I am, therefore, shy of these methods. But of recent years much close study has been given to the subject by such men as Mr. Noël Heaton, Mr. Warnes, and Professor Laurie, and it is likely that through their experience the main principles of this science will before long be understood and useful treatments discovered. The treatment which now seems to be meeting with general approval is that known by the name of Silicon-Ester. But it seems too early yet to pronounce definitely in its favour. Evidence as to the very many other advertised "preservative" liquids is conflicting. In one place Mr. X reports that liquid Y has been most efficient, in another it is known to have been useless or even harmful. In a word, in my opinion, chemical preservatives are still suspect. For this and other reasons no attempt is made to describe the proprietary liquids here. The cause of the failure of many "preservatives" 37 seems to be that they harden the outer skin of the stone, causing it to become brittle and peel or flake off. Something of the same sort happens in many building stones in the natural course of time. When first quarried, stone contains moisture known as "quarry sap," that is, the natural moisture in the stone. In this condition the stone is worked. The "quarry sap" makes its way to the surface and drys out. As it drys, it deposits near the surface, in the form of crystals, the natural cementing material of the stone which it carried in solution. Thus an outer hard skin or face is formed on the stone which withstands weather for a long time. When this skin is broken or decayed, the rain-carried agents of decay attack and disintegrate with increased speed the inner stone; more of the outer face is "blown off" or undermined, and decay is in full swing.

With regard to the theory of decay due to bacteria, the reader cannot do better than consult the treatise *Suggestions for the Prevention of the Decay of Building Stone* by Mr. J. E. Marsh which deals with this difficult subject. But while reading this he should bear in mind that Mr. Marsh's conclusions are not accepted by chemists without question or doubt. Mr. Warnes, for instance, while he thinks the theory should receive careful consideration, indicates that other sources exist which will explain the presence of the nitrates which, Mr. Marsh holds, indicate bacterial action or "life."

Mr. W. A. Forsyth observes that where rain falling from the surface of copper runs over stonework there is no decay. And from this he suggests that a preservative made from copper in solution would be useful. For this reason also he recommends copper rather than lead for covering cornices and the like projections.

38

The Ancient Monuments department of His Majesty's Office of Works has given the subject much attention, but as yet has not intimated that it is satisfied with any of the preservative liquids made by the chemists.

My own experience makes me, as already stated, shy of chemical treatment at present. The results obtained make one hopeful; but until the preservatives recommended have been tested over many years, and proved efficient, it is very doubtful whether they should be used otherwise than experimentally and on but small areas of ancient stonework. And when this is done a complete record of the work should be kept with the survey. Such points as the temperature of the stone at the time of application, the amount of moisture it contained, the exact nature of the preservative, should all be noted. And together with this, "close-up" photographs before treatment, immediately after it, and at least one in each succeeding year should be taken and filed. The information so obtained would be invaluable to those who are studying the subject.

Iron Set in Stone

Much damage is done to stonework by the presence of iron set into it. In the old days iron cramps were used to bind stone to stone, these being set either in the bed-joints or on the surface. The ends of window-bars are commonly found to have split the mullions and jambs.

Iron when it rusts expands with irresistible force and breaks asunder the masonry in which it is set. There is no need to go far in order to see this. In most streets where there are iron rails set in stone, the kerbs will be found to have split. It is this quality in iron and steel which causes a number of architects and some engineers to doubt the durability of concrete reinforced with iron, unless the iron is surrounded by an impervious material; they hold that concrete is insufficient protection. It is a safe rule always to remove iron from stonework, and to substitute for it copper, or one of the copper alloys, such as gunmetal or delta metal. Where the ironwork is in itself valuable, as are the medieval saddle and stanchion bars of windows, or the wrought-iron rails of the eighteenth century, it should be carefully taken out of the stonework, and new rustless metal ends should be welded on to the bars which are to be rebedded in the stone, and the whole

reset in cement mortar.   The welding of the copper alloys to
iron can be done by electric means.   At the joint between the
two metals electrolysis is encouraged, and the iron there rusts
away more quickly than elsewhere; but this damage is confined
to the metal and does not affect the stone.   Of recent years
sulphur has been used to set iron into stone.   It is hardly
necessary to note that this practice is pernicious.   Wherever
I have seen it used I have also found failure.

The removal of iron cramps from stonework is not always a
simple matter.   Although the intention should be to take every
piece out, and to substitute a rustless metal, there are cases
where as yet no rust has begun, and where, as a consequence,
the stone is as yet uninjured.   In these cases it may be well
to leave the ironwork undisturbed, for in its removal damage
may easily be done to the stonework.   In this regard it should
be remembered that medieval and eighteenth-century iron
has much less tendency to rust than modern.   Where it
has been determined to leave the iron in the stone, efforts
should be made to check the penetration of rain.   Often this
may be done by the use of good oil paint applied periodically
to the junction of the stone and iron.

THE USE OF DAMP-PROOF COURSES IN
OLD BUILDINGS

In every new building damp-proof courses are laid through
the thickness of the walls immediately above ground and in all
walls, be they chimneys or parapets, immediately above the
roofs.   In two cases, however, I have found traces of courses
of slate having the appearance of a damp-proof course laid in
the walls of a medieval building.   These traces were seen about
five feet above ground in the fifteenth-century work of Christ-
church Priory and in the unfinished early sixteenth-century
cloisters of Cleeve Abbey where one or two sections of the
walling are now exposed for the full thickness of the wall.

It is doubtful whether these courses of slate were indeed laid to prevent the rise or fall of moisture in the wall.

It is certainly desirable when repair work is being done to those parts of an ancient building where damp-proof courses are useful that they should be put in. But this is not all; sometimes they should be inserted in old walls for their own sake alone, not only to keep the inside dry, but to prevent the surface decay which an excess of moisture encourages. The exposed faces of wall tops are particularly liable to suffer in this way as may sometimes be seen in the top four or five feet of parapeted structures. It is difficult to decide whether or no damp-proof courses should be inserted in such cases, for one evil may be remedied at the cost of creating another. More of the interest and beauty of the affected surface of an ancient wall may be sacrificed, whether near the ground or at the level of a parapet, by disturbing it, than is worth while for the sake of freeing it from water. In parapets it is usually enough to see that the bed of the coping stones is impervious and that the two faces of the wall are properly pointed.

Damp working its way into a wall face below the ground, often due to concentrated saturation by roof water, has already been dealt with on general lines in the chapter on disposal of rain-water, to which reference should be made. Here the insertion of horizontal damp-proof courses alone will be discussed.

Probably the form of damp-proof course most suitable for the mortar-built walls of monumental architecture is the one laid in the material of the same general nature, that is, the double course of slate laid in cement mortar. Mr. Thackeray Turner recommends sheet lead, because it can be unrolled easily, is continuous, and, if laid on an even bed, is not cracked or broken during the process of pinning up to the work above. 39

The same principles apply to the form of damp-proof courses in old walls as apply to those in new. The decision whether or no such a course should be put in rests on cost and on the harm the alteration may do or the changes it may make to the qualities which give value to the building.

There is no more difficulty in cutting out for a damp course and building it in than there is in cutting out loose work and repairing the wall by "building." In both cases only small pieces of work can be done at a time and in both cases the walling adjoining the part treated should not be touched until the new work has set. The bed on which the damp course is laid should be smooth and level or stepped in a series of levels. When a wall is cut out for a damp course it may be well to take the opportunity to build a strengthening belt for the length of the wall.

A machine has been invented for laying damp courses in lime-built brick walls, or walls that are soft enough to be cut with the saw which forms part of the machine. But this machine does not appear to have been much used, though a claim is made for it that it causes little disturbance to walls.

For vertical damp courses underground, asphalt laid in two thicknesses on properly prepared walls seems to be the best. Owing to the fact that the laying of asphalt requires expert men and special plant, neither easily to be had in country places without undue expense, it is not uncommon to rely on waterproofed cement rendering or vertical slate in cement damp courses for this work. These when they fail do so more because proper preparation is not made for them than because of any intrinsic fault. The reason for this seems to be that a builder will take more trouble to prepare for an expensive and unfamiliar material than he will for one which he constantly handles.

Although damp cannot be certainly prevented from rising in a wall from the soil unless a horizontal damp-proof course is put in, much can be done both within and without by taking all other precautions. Thus a joist floor laid within a building may be rendered immune from such defects by being laid with a ventilated air space beneath, above an impervious bed of concrete and separated from the walls themselves by a vertical damp-proof course. In such a case joinery, as panelling, bench ends, or skirtings may also be separated from the walls either by a damp-proof course or a sufficient air space.

The Knapen system of drawing damp from walls by means of capillary tubes should be mentioned. Although it has not been generally adopted, this system is likely to prove useful. ⁴⁰

In timber framed buildings the damp-proof course can conveniently be laid beneath the timber sill on which the uprights are set.

Paved Floors

In churches, when the paving is laid direct on the earth or where boarding under pews is laid on joists placed on the ground, it is usual but not always desirable that the floor should be taken up and relaid. In relaying old paving the stones should be preserved and relaid in exactly the same positions as they are found. With this in view the stones should be marked and a plan made of their arrangement before they are raised. Cracked stones can be relaid, for such defects are little disadvantage to a floor that is properly set on a solid concrete bed. Sometimes badly-worn stones may be reversed. Old memorial slabs should be relaid exactly where they are found, unless it is certainly known that they have been moved before and their original position cannot be ascertained. Old paving tiles and brick, once the common product of a district, should also be preserved for re-use, for others of like kind are now difficult to obtain. They belong to a different tradition of tile-making than that followed to-day. When it is decided to relay the whole floor in a church or other large hall, after making notes of what exists, the floor covering may be raised and set aside for re-use. The area then should be excavated and covered completely with six inches of clean hardcore broken to the size of ordinary road metalling. On this the concrete may be laid to the required levels. The concrete should be sound Portland cement concrete mixed as is usual for modern work. It is good practice to lay the paving stones and tiles in cement mortar, but to point them in lime mortar, since the latter material accords with the old custom. When such a floor is being relaid, the encaustic tiles made in the ⁴¹

nineteenth century, which remind one of the entrance halls of
modern provincial hotels, may be disposed of and other paving
less different from the older kind may be used instead.   The
original floor and step levels should be carefully studied and,
if practicable, recovered; especially is this the case in churches.
Sometimes, however, an arrangement that is later than that of
the building itself has marked individual interest and should
be preserved for its own sake.   While excavation is being
made for the new hardcore and concrete the surface ground
should be sifted or otherwise carefully examined, for interesting
pieces of old glass and other objects of art are commonly found
42 in the top layers of earth there.

PUTNEY PARISH CHURCH
THE AMOUNT NEEDED FOR THE RENOVATION OF THIS ANCIENT PARISH CHURCH IS AT LEAST £3000
PLEASE HELP BY SENDING A DONATION TO THE VICAR OR THE CHURCH WARDENS
AMOUNT ALREADY RECEIVED £2590
AMOUNT STILL REQUIRED — £410

FIG. 21. THE TOWER OF PUTNEY CHURCH AFTER POINTING WITH BLACK CEMENT WITH RAISED RIBBON JOINTS

THE SIXTH CHAPTER

THE REPAIR OF ANCIENT TIMBER ROOFS AND OTHER WORKS OF FINE CARPENTRY

General

As in the case of repair to masonry and brickwork the object of those who wish to maintain timber constructions is the repair of the individual members rather than a vague regard for the whole, since the latter is apt to be followed by too much renewal.

The same procedure should be followed in the repair of carpentry as in other parts of a building. The order of work will be influenced by such features as a valuable ceiling or by ancient coloured decoration or by the acquired character of the covering.

The cause of leaks in the roof, whether they are due to temporary defects in materials or to fundamental faults in design, should be noted in the survey.

Temporary Covering During Work

When a roof covering has to be disturbed for repair, the parts of the building thus exposed must be protected from weather during the work. Particular care should be taken to secure that old walls and old timbers are not exposed to rain. Convenient covering may be provided by using tarpaulins or by the erection of shelters of corrugated iron or other temporary material. The choice of one or other form of temporary covering depends on the question of which is the more economical. It takes time morning and night to withdraw and relay tarpaulins, and also, unless carefully relaid and held in position, they may be the cause of flooding, particularly in windy weather.   Whatever form of covering is used it should be arranged so as to throw rain-water clear of the walls of a building.   When a raised shelter is used it should be arranged at such a height above the old roof as to allow for men to work below it, and it may be made so that it can be easily moved to cover one section after another as the work proceeds.   43

The Survey

The preliminary survey of the timber roof of a great hall or church is a long and rather costly matter, for the condition of the timbers cannot be known unless they are seen at close quarters.   For this long ladders are necessary and sometimes scaffolding.   Survey from within can be supplemented by examination from without; some tiles may be stripped or lead turned back at suspected points.   Many timbers have been and many still continue to be condemned too readily as rotten throughout, when in reality only the sap-wood was or is defective.   The outer one and a half inches of an oak log is always sapwood and in cutting big timbers from a tree which is not straight patches of sap-wood are often left on the edges.   It often was and is rightly still the custom, in order to avoid waste of timber, not to worry if the big pieces used in carpentry do not hold their full section free from sap for their whole length, but in every case the sap-wood should be cut away from both new and old timber.   Indeed it seems that the beautiful chamfers so often given to the edges of beams wrought in the medieval tradition had their origin in this wise precaution. Sap-wood may be recognised by its pale colour.   It is always the first part attacked by worm and it is not unlikely that its presence attracts the beetle whose larvæ they are.   An experienced timber merchant advised me not to use the centre wood of big trees, and my experience is that the very heart of an old tree is almost as liable to attack from wood-worm as is sap-wood itself.   In the fine oak roof above King's   44 College Chapel at Cambridge a brief inspection revealed neither sap nor worm; and it may be that the timbers of this roof are cut from either side of the very centre of the trees which were felled for the purpose; it is also very well ventilated. If a timber appears rotten on the surface, before assuming that it is so throughout, it will be useful to test it with a gimlet. Further, before condemning a timber that is even much decayed it is well to think whether a greater section than the remaining sound wood would be used in modern work; in other words, whether the remaining timber is not strong enough to do the work it was meant to do. The unseen ends of old beams which are bedded in walls, cannot be assumed to be sound until the wall has been opened out about them. For it is at this point that the wood-worm is found to be particularly active. No survey of a timber framed structure can be accepted as a sure basis on which to prepare a close estimate of the cost of repair. It is inevitable that much must be left unknown until all the timbers are exposed. General experience is the best guide in estimating.

The Size of Timbers to be Used on Repair Works

The Society for the Protection of Ancient Buildings recommends that when new timbers are added to an ancient roof they should be worked simply without enrichment which may compete, by comparison, with the old. Further, it advises that when a new timber is needed to take the place of one that is too much decayed to be repaired, it should not be carved like the old and that the main lines of the mouldings only should be repeated.

Medieval builders allowed such an enormous margin of safety in the timbers they used that even when these suffer from decay, the remainder may for long be sufficient to maintain equilibrium. In the repair of their buildings their example as regards safety should be followed. It is better to repair a portion of a roof in their generous manner and to support the remainder with temporary props pending later opportunity, than to continue the work throughout the whole in a less substantial way.

It is a general principle that roofs of timber should be re-paired with like material, but iron, steel or other metals may be used sometimes to strengthen a joint between old and new or to reinforce an ancient timber or even a whole framework.   45

Causes of Failure

Carpentry fails from many causes of which the following are the more common:

(1) Constructional faults: these may be due either (*a*) to poor design, (*b*) to too slight timbers, (*c*) to mutilation done after the work is complete, and more rarely, (*d*) to loss of nature in the timber itself.

(2) Rot due to various reasons: (*a*) to the action of insects, chiefly the larvae of the death watch and the furniture beetles, (*b*) the growth of various fungi (dry rot), and (*c*) to the constant expansion and contraction caused by alternate saturation and drying out.

Structural

In roofs the constructive defect most commonly found is the want of adequate means to resist the outward thrust of the two slopes. Here, as in arched masonry, "drift" as well as thrust must be withstood. Many medieval roofs were designed without tie-beams, particularly those which are of the hammer-beam kind. In these cases it is desirable to make sure that the roofs are designed or strengthened so that only a direct vertical load comes on to the walls, and this is the more desirable when the walls are old and already weakened by fractures or by leaning over a little. The medieval builders in their desire to have high open roofs unbroken by tie-beams from wall to wall sometimes made roofs which through the centuries have spread outward, carrying the walls with them. Although we may regret to change an old design by the addition of tie-beams or -rods, such new members should be added when, because of their absence, strain has come on old roof timbers

and on the joints between them. The eventual loss of the
original timbers of an old roof and the weakening of walls consequent on the want of tie-beams or -rods is far more serious
than the change caused by the addition of a suitable tie.

The parts of a roof which are the first to decay are noted
below and these are also indicative of the parts which in other
frameworks are often defective: The ends of rafters, especially
their feet, wall plates, the wall ends of tie- or hammer-beams,
the backs of cornice planks and wall legs, the tenons of purlins
and the mortise holes that take them, the backs of principal
rafters that are close-boarded, and the ends of beams built
into walls.

English oak should be used for the repair of a roof originally
framed of this wood. Seasoned timber, which is now hard to
get in large sizes, should be used for the members which would
suffer from the results of shrinking, particularly is this so for
those timbers which abut diagonally against others, as do most
bracing-pieces. It is not so important that common rafters
which lie comparatively free on the framed roof trusses and
purlins should be seasoned; again, in very simple framed constructions seasoning is not so important as in more complicated
structures. One disadvantage of unseasoned timber, particularly when it contains the centre of a tree, is that it "shakes"
or cracks longitudinally. These cracks do not usually much
reduce the strength but they provide crevices that are ideal
nurseries for the progeny of the timber beetles.

Common Methods of Repair

If a roof is taken right down for repair much more is lost than
if it is repaired in position; again, similar loss of old work is
found to happen unless a roof is repaired bay by bay. Thus
the procedure usually should be (1) to strip the covering from
the portion to be repaired; (2) to remove the boarding carefully
and store under cover for re-use; (3) to remove the rafters and
repair them on the staging immediately below the roof, number-
ing them so that they may be again placed in the same positions

FIG. 22. PENSHURST PLACE. ROOF OF BARON'S HALL DURING REPAIR BY MR. WM. WEIR

FIG. 23. PENSHURST PLACE. ROOF OF BARON'S HALL AFTER REPAIR BY MR. WM. WEIR

they originally held; (4) the purlins, or at least some of them, can usually be repaired without moving them from their positions; (5) every effort should be made to repair the timbers of framed trusses in position.

Every defect in the members of a roof needs its own special treatment, yet certain methods of repair are general and with slight modifications may be applied in most cases.

Rafters

As a rule it is possible by renewing a certain number of rafters to repair the remainder by lengthening them with wood cut from the old rafters that have been rejected. In this case the joints should if possible be made above the purlins, and the joint may be a simple scarf, the two pieces being bolted. (See Fig. 24, A.)

In coupled-rafter roofs where the tops of the rafters are becoming defective it may be convenient in the interests of economy to strengthen the junctions of rafter and rafter without adding new tops. This has been done by spiking pieces of one inch thick and nine inch wide planking on each side a little below the ridge. (See Fig. 24, B.)

Wall-Plates

Wall-plates are the timbers which lie on the wall top to take the feet of rafters. They may rest on the ends of tie-beams and span the space between them, or in some earlier coupled-rafter roofs they may lie across the thickness of the wall on a couple of longitudinal plates. Frequently these members of a roof are further decayed than any others. This is due to the fact that they are often surrounded by mortar or dirt, sometimes even they are found to be buried in earth. Ventilation is essential to long life in timber. Therefore the wall top must first be cleaned of all rubbish and dirt and must be made sound and level with concrete or otherwise so that new and old timbers may be free on all sides to the air. Often wall-plates need entire renewal. They are a vital part of a roof and should be continuous from tie-beam to tie-beam. They should be of such section as will best resist buckling outward in a horizontal plane between the tie-beams, and they must be securely fixed to the tie-beams or -rods to resist the outward thrust of the roof. Elaborate and expensive as well as simple

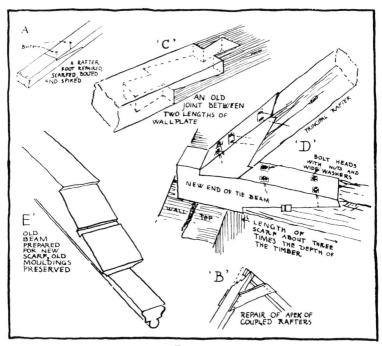

FIG. 24

joints are found between lengths of wall-plates in old roofs. An example of the former kind is shown in Fig. 24, c.

Tie-beams and Hammer-beams

The ends of these are commonly defective owing to the same causes of decay as are present in wall-plates. As a rule repair may be made by scarfing on new ends; sometimes iron or steel flitch-plates are used instead. The accompanying sketches show the methods. (See Figs. 24, D.) The Society for the

Protection of Ancient Buildings recommends new ends of English oak as preferable to repair with iron, but it is not always possible to avoid ironwork and sometimes by its use more old timber is preserved than could otherwise be the case. It is Mr. Weir's practice to scarf on new ends.

As a rule in this position more of the old moulding of the tie-beam may be preserved by putting the short length of the new scarf on the underside and the long part on the upper, which is contrary to the usual practice of commercial work. For the sake of clarity in these sketches mouldings are not shown. In a richly moulded beam the moulding or at least the lower mouldings of the old beam may sometimes be preserved by scarfing the old timber in the way suggested in Fig. 24, E. But what can or cannot be done will always depend on the amount of rotted wood which has to be cut away. The sketches (see Fig. 24) are intended to be suggestive of methods of repair and are not to be taken as final.

Sometimes it may be found convenient to cut a roll moulding off and to spike or screw it on again after the scarf is made.

Principal Rafters

In Fig. 24, D, a new foot is shown scarfed on to a principal rafter, but these members of a roof are also often found to be defective at the points where they are mortised to the purlins; in such cases it may be possible to insert a new piece of oak, somewhat as shown in Fig. 25. Such piecing may also be strengthened with ironwork. In this figure the hatching represents new timber laid in in three pieces; each piece may conveniently be a little wider than the beam to be repaired. Each piece should be cut wedge-shape and tapped into position from the side, and the joint made tight by saw-cuts during the process. Each piece when in position should be screwed to the old beam or piece below, and when all are in position the whole may be bolted up with an iron tension-strap. The pieces may be put in from alternate sides. When all is bolted up the new timber may be trimmed to the thickness of the beam.

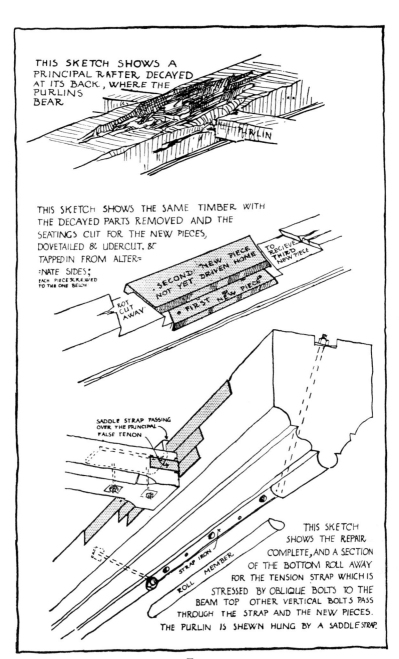

THIS SKETCH SHOWS A PRINCIPAL RAFTER DECAYED AT ITS BACK, WHERE THE PURLINS BEAR

THIS SKETCH SHOWS THE SAME TIMBER WITH THE DECAYED PARTS REMOVED AND THE SEATINGS CUT FOR THE NEW PIECES, DOVETAILED & UDERCUT, & TAPPED IN FROM ALTER= =NATE SIDES; EACH PIECE SCREWED TO THE ONE BELOW

PURLIN

TO RECIEVE THIRD NEW PIECE

"SECOND" NEW PIECE NOT YET DRIVEN HOME

"FIRST" NEW PIECE

ROT CUT AWAY

SADDLE STRAP PASSING OVER THE PRINCIPAL FALSE TENON

STRAP IRON

ROLL MEMBER

THIS SKETCH SHOWS THE REPAIR COMPLETE, AND A SECTION OF THE BOTTOM ROLL AWAY FOR THE TENSION STRAP WHICH IS STRESSED BY OBLIQUE BOLTS TO THE BEAM TOP OTHER VERTICAL BOLTS PASS THROUGH THE STRAP AND THE NEW PIECES. THE PURLIN IS SHEWN HUNG BY A SADDLE STRAP.

FIG. 25

Mr. William Weir often cuts out the rotted wood from above, leaving the sound cheeks of the beam, and inserts sound oak

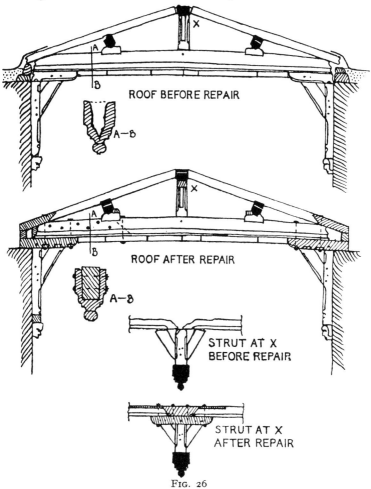

ROOF BEFORE REPAIR

A—B

ROOF AFTER REPAIR

A—B

STRUT AT X
BEFORE REPAIR

STRUT AT X
AFTER REPAIR

FIG. 26

in the space so made. The renewal of the core of an old timber in this way is illustrated here in conjunction with the repair of a low-pitched roof. The hollow space in the back and in the heart of the oak was turned to advantage for gaining the additional strength required. (See Fig. 26.)   Seasoned timber is necessary in these cases.

Purlins

Purlins, the horizontal timbers supporting the rafters and spanning the space between the principal rafters, may be repaired as the other members of a roof already referred to. Like other timbers purlins decay first at their ends and often before they have lost strength the tenon by which they are supported turns to powder owing to the activity of wood-worm.   The usual method of repair is by strap-irons and false tenons, as shown in Fig. 25.

Other Timbers

Wall legs, the upright timbers, sometimes resting on corbels, which stand out from the wall beneath tie- or hammer-beams —these timbers and others which back on to walling suffer severely from the ravages of wood-worm.   That insect thrives in just such dark and sheltered positions as the narrow space between wall and timber.   Repair may be carried out by sawing off the back of these timbers and substituting new sound oak. A further precaution is important; the back of the new timber should be kept just free of the wall and plaster.   For structural reasons the back must press on the wall, and provision can be made for this by allowing two or three stones to project against the back of the timber, or by fixing at intervals oak fillets on the back.   Timber cornice members at the wall top and between the principal rafters of medieval roofs may often be treated similarly to wall legs.

The Ends of Beams in Walls

Where old beam ends are built into walls or where new ends are put to take the place of old in this position they should never be built in closely with mortar and masonry.   Always there should be space about the ends for ventilation, and this may be provided by forming clean pockets of concrete or masonry at least two inches wider and deeper and higher than the timber to be placed there. Where the beam so placed has to carry a moving load it may be wedged tight with dry slates driven in, but even in these cases no mortar should be allowed to come in contact with the timber.

46

The Use of Iron and Steel in the Repair of Ancient Timber Framed Constructions

Iron and steel, though useful sometimes, should be avoided in the repair of ancient timber framed constructions where new oak will serve the purpose. There are occasions where one or other of these metals is desirable: (1) where very much more of the old work can be preserved without unsightliness by this use; (2) where the size of the timbers to be repaired makes the cost of using oak prohibitive.

Both these conditions were present in the case of the roof of Westminster Hall lately repaired and strengthened with steel by His Majesty's Office of Works under the advice of Sir Frank Baines. This work was very well done; I do not see that any other means could have been adopted. We may regret to know that so fine a roof no longer has its full constructional significance. In this work it cannot be said that the roof is hung from an almost hidden steel frame, for without the oak-work I doubt if the steel-work would stand. Metal was used to strengthen, not to replace the structural members of the old roof. Possibly an apt simile would be to liken the present state of this, the finest piece of carpentry ever done by man, to a living lion caged for show as opposed to the beast roaming freely the foothills of Kenya Mountain.

Steel and iron, then, have their uses in the repair of timber. They are necessary as bolts where a beam is scarfed; rods are sometimes desirable to tie together the feet of spreading principal rafters. It can hardly, then, be questioned that these materials occasionally should be used elsewhere, and this in spite of the knowledge that hidden ironwork cannot receive the attention it needs for its preservation. It is known that the great hidden steel stanchions of American sky-scrapers have been found to have rusted through in less than twenty years: but while such cases are exceptional, they should be remembered, and in monumental buildings ferruginous metals should be used sparingly and with caution, and with as great a margin of safety as the medieval builders provided in their timbers.

Some architects prefer to strengthen tie-beams and other of the greater structural timbers with iron flitch plates rather than to scarf new ends on to them, and this practice may be recommended when by its adoption more of the old timber is preserved than would otherwise be. Mr. William Weir has, however, told me that he has never come across a case in his practice where it has been desirable to use flitch plates.

But perhaps before long structural ironwork as rustless as stainless knives will be prepared on a commercial basis.

Enough has been written here to suggest ways of repairs to other timber-work than roofs. Floors, framed walls, galleries, and such structures may all be treated on lines not dissimilar.

West Walton Church

The two accompanying illustrations (Figs. 27 and 28) of the roof repair of West Walton Church will be the better understood for some description. In the photograph taken from outside the church it will be seen that part of the roof is repaired and the newly recast lead is being laid there. It may be noted that the horizontal or lap-joints of the lead are staggered, and I think the sheets of lead are being laid a little askew with the eaves. One bay is undergoing repair, and the protective tarpaulins are rolled back for the work. In this portion of the roof a new wall plate can be seen, and the tail of a new end of one of the hammer-beams.

FIG. 27. WEST WALTON CHURCH FROM THE SOUTH DURING REPAIR, 1907

FIG. 28. WEST WALTON CHURCH. THE NAVE ROOF AFTER REPAIR, 1907

Beyond—farther west—the old roof though uncovered has not been disturbed.   It will be seen that the wall plate had quite disappeared, and many rafter feet with it.   Farther west still, in the untouched roof the oak "cladding" laid with joints of about one inch may be seen projecting below the untouched lead.

In the photograph taken from within the church, a portion of the repaired work may be seen.   A new rafter with the circular saw marks may be seen in the centre of the roof-bay that is shown.   There was about one of these to each bay and the other rafters were made by scarfing together the remaining sound timbers.   Only a very small portion of the new end to the hammer-beam can be seen in this photograph. More is to be seen in other of the beams where rot was worse. The raw deal boarding is visible between the old oak "cladding" where before the repair the underside of the lead sheet was visible.

It will be seen from the spacing of the bays that the roof may not have been designed for this church and further evidence of this is to be noticed in the church, for in some places the embattled cornice - board, the straining - piece between the hammer-beams, is a number of inches away from the wall. Traces of coloured decoration may be seen in the thirteenth-century window arch.

Rot and its Prevention

No suggestion for the repair of timber structures should be left without reference to ways by which the active agencies of decay — wood-worm, dry-rot, and rot due to alternate periods of wet and dry—may be checked.

Wood-worm

Since the repair of the magnificent roof of Westminster Hall the damage done by the larvæ of the death-watch beetle— Xestobium tessellatum—and of the lesser death-watch beetle, 48 in old days known respectively as wood-worm and furniture-worm, has received scientific study and excited public attention. To-day the guardians of ancient roofs can be frightened into making drastic and expensive renewals by the very mention of this insect, something in the same way as men and women were persuaded to offer themselves as material for the surgeon's skill when appendicitis was newly a subject for paragraphs in every newspaper. The disease is serious. But the discovery of worm-holes in timber is not of itself warning of instant collapse. There is hardly any old timber construction that is not affected. The mark of the insect can be seen on the dead knots and limbs of every growing tree and on many a gate-post that has stood in the open for more than fifteen or twenty years. From ages before man first built shelters for his kind, the beetle no less than moth or rust has caused slow corruption. Man can hinder but he cannot prevent ultimate decay.

In spite of the fact that this maggot gets sustenance from dead wood in the open air, evidence seems to show that he thrives best in dim and confined spaces. It appears that he is most active where the dirt of neglect lies undisturbed for years. Therefore it is thought that the two most effectual checks to his activity are cleanliness and ventilation. Roofs should be swept clean at regular intervals, especially those parts most difficult of access—the timbers at wall tops and above ceilings. A vacuum-cleaner should be used wherever it is available, for with it this cleaning can be done more thoroughly.

The indifference of our ancestors to draughts allowed them to suffer the wind to blow through roofs with little hindrance, but the modern insistence on greater comfort has brought with it the practice of warming ancient buildings to a degree un-known in old days. Now that felt is often laid below tiles and lead alike, and all holes and cracks through which the outer air penetrated are stopped, the heating engineer when he makes his tests can report a wonderful rise in the temperature within a building. The stuffy heat that is felt in high roofs seems to provide the beetle with exactly that atmosphere in which he most quickly multiplies. With modern changes, the old balance of life is disturbed and at each advance a new adjustment has to be made. Thus where increased comfort is certainly followed by the hastened corruption of noble timbering, it is necessary with the provision of the first to resist by new means the more rapid progress of the second.

With this object the scientists of to-day have experimented and, as a result of investigation, invented solutions which materially check, if they do not ultimately prevent, the breeding of this insect. Professor Lefroy in his enthusiastic efforts to this end sacrificed his life during the search for more certain preventives. Yet before he died he gave the world a greatly increased knowledge of the subject. Sir Frank Baines with the help of Messrs. Heppel devised a liquid useful to check the ravages of this pest. Both preparations are good, either should be used freely whenever a timber construction is under repair. Each beam, each joint should be treated and the printed instructions which approved makers send out with their preparations should be carefully followed. The liquids which at present the Society for the Protection of Ancient Buildings recommends for this purpose are those prepared by Messrs. Heppel, by Kenford Ltd., and by the Disinfectant and General Products Company. The Society also recommends a preparation prescribed for it by Mr. Noël Heaton. It is, however, advisable before ordering the application of a liquid throughout a structure to treat a portion only, so as to make certain that no undue change of colour follows the operation. 49

The authorities of South Kensington Museum have found it useful to treat fine joinery and furniture with a preparation made by dissolving a quarter of a pound of parchment cuttings in a quarter of a gallon of boiling water. This liquid is applied with a brush or spray, allowing it to sink well into the wood. Any of this parchment size which remains on the surface should be sponged off after the application has been made, and finally a little beeswax and turpentine can be applied. Again, for furniture and fine joinery bichloride of mercury is sometimes injected into the wormholes with a hypodermic syringe, but

as this liquid is dangerous to those who use it, special precautions must be taken.

It may be observed that furniture that is constantly dusted
back and front and moved about is not subject to the attack
of either beetle, and from this it may be concluded that such
regular cleaning will ensure safety. Therefore where it is
possible to arrange that even big structural timbers may be
regularly rubbed over they will be free from attack. For this
purpose it is well to order that a little beeswax be used, partly
because it actually does protect the wood and partly because
those employed in rubbing the surface of timber will do it
more thoroughly when they apply wax than when they are
told to rub alone. But only a little wax should ever be applied.

Many people, particularly the amateur lovers of ancient
buildings, like to use preservative liquids to darken oak. This
is a mistake. The natural colour of oak is beautiful, and
when it has aged it becomes more so. Any new timber can be
stained dark, but the tone acquired by age is a thing difficult
to get, and one which it is a shame artificially to alter.

Dry Rot

There is still confusion in the minds of many as to how dry
rot may be recognised. The dry powdering of wood, especially
of sap-wood, which accompanies the activities of wood-worm
is sometimes wrongly described as dry rot by those unfamiliar
with its real nature. Dry rot is the condition of timber which
is giving nourishment to certain fungi and particularly that
known as Merculius lachrymans. The fungus spreads rapidly,
and when discovered the affected timbers and the walling
near by should at once be treated. It is the regular practice
in commercial work to remove and burn the infected wood,
except in the very initial stages. In initial stages of the rot
the following preparations are recommended, and all the
timbers and walling near the affected part should also be
treated.

The most effective preventive is a five per cent solution of corrosive sublimate in water, but it is poisonous and should only be used by those who understand its dangers and can be trusted to take proper precautions against them.   A less effective, but safe solution is five pounds of zinc sulphate dissolved in a gallon of water.   Again, three-quarters of a pound of sulphate of copper dissolved in one gallon of water is useful, but this should not be used from a metal container.   It should be brushed or sprayed on.   A surface treatment with creosote is also useful, but as this discolours timbers it is not everywhere a suitable material.   Picric acid may also be used successfully but again it affects the colour, turning everything to which it is applied a brown gold.   51

Ordinary Rot

Rot due to alternate wet and dry can only be checked by making sure that the timber affected is kept quite dry or permanently immersed in water.   The former case is the one which concerns the structural timbers of building, and the cure is nothing more than to prevent moisture penetrating through roofs and walls or rising from the ground.   It seems also that the wood-worm is especially active where timber is occasionally wetted owing to leaks in the roof covering.

Hardening Frail Carving

It has been suggested that carved or moulded woodwork that has become frail through one or other form of rot may be hardened and to a certain extent consolidated by applying a solution of magnesium fluosilicate—one pound of salts to a gallon of water to make the solution.   52

The Treatment of bad '' Shakes ''

It has been remarked that open "shakes," that is, the splits which appear in big timbers during seasoning where they are exposed to weather, may encourage rot by allowing rain to reach the heart of the wood. In such positions when "shakes" are bad, they should be stopped, and the following sentences may be of use in suggesting a way of doing this.

Of old it was sometimes the custom to stop these crevices with run putty mixed with hair. But it seems that this is not a very satisfactory method, for putty does not altogether check the entry of water and when once set has little or no ability to expand and contract with any seasonal movement which may take place in the timber. It would seem preferable to caulk these cracks as the decks of ships are caulked with bituminous mastic and hemp. Where the shakes are very wide it may be well to fill them with strips of dry oak bedded in this material. Under shelter, so long as "shakes" do not materially weaken timbers they are harmless except as affording the beetle convenient crevices wherein to lay her eggs.

Timber Floors

The repair of the timber joist-floors is like that of timber roofs, and there is but little to be said of other floors in ancient buildings than what is to be found in books on building construction. I remember seeing the late Mr. Ernest Gimson lay a new floor in the dining-room at Sheffield Park. It was a beautiful piece of work when finished. He used fine wide boards thoroughly seasoned; some of them were cut from a tree which tapered more than usual and these he laid together with the butt-ends reversed. This floor had a proper air space beneath and all the boards were painted in two or three coats with red-lead paint on the underside. Except that every precaution was taken to make the floor a good one and that great care was taken in laying it, it did not differ from others, but the greater beauty of the finished work was very marked.

The floors of old buildings are often out of true level and this fact is one which gives a sense of age more quickly, yet less obviously, than almost any other feature. Except where a truly level floor is desired for particular purposes there is no need to disturb such irregularities.

The timber joist-floors of an old house are usually covered with wide oak boards which are commonly rebated. It is often found that the upper rebate has worn away or been split off or that the joint between board and board is open. In such a case it is a good plan to caulk the joints as are those of a ship's deck.   53

Solid Wood Floors

It is a modern practice to lay wood block floors in old buildings: this is not recommended by the Society for the Protection of Ancient Buildings, on the ground that block floors are inappropriate and are much more suggestive of a new school hall than fit for an old-time building. The alternative is to lay a boarded floor, and preferably one of well-seasoned oak, chestnut, or other hard wood. Such floors can, if proper care is taken, be laid solid in mastic just as are wood blocks, but in addition the boards must be nailed to *clean* breeze concrete,   54 or better, to breeze concrete joists laid on the concrete underfloor. It is well, however, to leave the concrete underfloor longer time to dry out than is usual before a wood block is laid on it; for, unless this precaution is taken, the boarding is apt to swell when laid and to shrink badly. A year is not too long to wait; and in a monumental building time should be regarded in relation to the building and not to the span of a man's life.

Where boarding is laid on joists above concrete, proper ventilation beneath it should of course be provided. The concrete is best laid on hardcore as before described.

Flagstaffs on Towers

A flagpole stayed from a turret or from the battlements of a church tower will loosen and damage the masonry to which it is attached. When this arrangement exists it should be altered and better fixing provided from well within the tower. In the photographs of Kingston Church tower, Somerset

(Figs. 29, 30, and 31), it will be seen that the flagpole was fixed in the way condemned here and that it is now refixed as it should be. Apart from the damage done by a flagpole when stayed from battlements, it cannot be conveniently lowered, and such an arrangement makes it difficult and awkward to repaint or to repair a broken flag cord.

The method which has been found satisfactory in all respects is to fix the flagpole to a central stay-post with metal hold-fasts which can be detached by the removal of a nut near the top of the stay-post and another just above the roof. When a pole is so arranged it is easy to lower it for repairs or painting. It is the provision and fixing of the stay-post which requires special care and attention. This post should be about six inches square of English oak. It should stand at least six feet above the roof and should descend at least six feet below the roof beams. The weight of the post may be taken at its very foot by a special stout oak beam spanning right across the tower from wall to wall, or it may be taken by the central roof beam. If the weight is taken at the roof-level the bottom end of the stay-post may be held upright by iron tie-rods anchored in the four walls of the tower, or by diagonal bracing-struts springing from the foot of the stay-post to the roof timbers. In a church tower a beam at this level at the foot of the stay-post is, however, often useful to take tackle for raising and lowering the bells. The junction of such a stay-post with the roof covering is often a point where slight leaks occur. It is usual to turn the lead sheets with which the roof is covered three inches or so up it and to close nail a lead flashing above this on to the stay-post. A more permanent way to secure this joint is to cover the stay-post with lead or copper, and in this case the metal holdfasts are fixed after the lead or copper is put on. Precautions, however, must be taken to shield a lead covering from the action of the tannic acid in oak.

55

FIG. 29.   KINGSTON, SOMERSET, THE CHURCH

FIG. 30. PARAPET SPLIT BY IRONWORK

FIG. 31. PARAPET AFTER REPAIR, IRONWORK REMOVED AND
GUNMETAL SUBSTITUTED

THE SEVENTH CHAPTER

ROOF COVERINGS

Buildings covered with old plain or pan tiles or with old slates or stone tiles or with lead or thatch derive much of their beauty and individual character from these materials, and for this reason these materials should be preserved or replaced by new of like kind.

Common Defects of Roof Coverings

Defects in tiled and slated roofs are usually due to one or other of the following causes. Either the tiling laths or the nails by which they are fixed to the rafters have become defective or the pegs or nails by which the covering itself is hung on the roof have decayed. In all these cases the covering tends to slip down the roof either in patches or single tiles. When the covering looks loose, its condition should be examined from below and the tiling laths and pins inspected. When either are found seriously at fault the roof should be stripped, the covering tiles cleaned, sorted in like sizes and stored, and the roof timbers prepared to receive them again. Often it is wise to deal with a roof in sections and not strip the whole at one time. Such extra tiles or slates as are needed to make up for deficiencies should be newly made or quarried and not taken from other old roofs in the neighbourhood; for by that action, which is now unfortunately common, the countryside is losing much of its beauty. Fired clay tiles are still made in the old way by some firms and these should be made specially of the same shapes and thickness as the old. If the character of an ancient roof is to be maintained it is important that

machine-made tiles should not be used in the place of hand-
made. Many machine-made tiles also are liable to flake owing to
the action of frost. Old plain tiles were usually a little concave
on the underside, a form technically known as "double cambered"; they were also thicker than modern tiles, in fact
medieval tiles were about three-quarters of an inch thick.
From these qualities they derive their special beauty. It is
sometimes desirable to procure enough new tiles for the work
before the stripping of the roof is begun, and thus avoid the
alternatives of either waiting for new tiles while the roof is
stripped of the old or of using materials that are not entirely
suitable, but which can be obtained without delay.

56   Stone tiles are still quarried in many parts of the country,
and are quite as good as any that are on old roofs. At Swanage
in Dorset, in the Chilmark district of Wiltshire, at Castlecombe
in Wiltshire, at Guiting in Gloucestershire and elsewhere these
tiles may still be had new.

Both stone and fired tiles, if the latter be made in the old
way, will "weather" just as the old in three to five years, so that
the desire that roofs should "look old" at once is very nearly
as well satisfied as by using old tiles, whilst other old roofs are
not destroyed.

Occasionally a roof is found to be defective because the
original design has been modified, or was at fault. Errors
of design are seldom found in earlier work. Sometimes,
however, they occur where a medieval roof has been reconstructed in a later century, sometimes when the covering
material has been changed. A defect in design more common
than others is insufficient pitch. The general practice of the
old builders was to use steeper pitches than are now in use.
Thus thatch was never laid on roofs with a pitch of less than
50° while for fired tiles the pitch was usually at 52°. Roofs
covered with stone slates were given a variety of slopes according to the nature of the slabs used; thus in Gloucestershire the
common pitch is 50° and in Yorkshire where the slabs are
larger it was even less than 45°. Lead was laid on roofs
which had very slight or very steep slopes, and sometimes

where it has been replaced by slates the pitch was too little for that material and the roof has consequently proved defective.

The pitch of a roof is important in considering repair works. It is useless, for instance, to attempt to reinstate tiles on a low-pitched roof or to lay thatch on roofs which slope less than traditional practice permits.

Another fault of tiled and slated roofs that is sometimes found is insufficient lap of one row over another, and this can only be put right by stripping and relaying.

Again, want of ventilation in all parts of a roof is a reason why tiling laths and pins, to say nothing of the structural timbers themselves, decay before their proper life is ended.

Excess of moss on tiled, stone tiled, and slated roofs is harmful and should be removed, but lichens do not hurt, take very long to grow and are beautiful in colour. Therefore they should be preserved. Ivy and creepers allowed to grow over roofs very quickly lift the tiles and create leaks; however beautiful these plants may appear to be, if a building is of value, they should be ruthlessly cut down.

The survey of a building should contain an account of the roof covering, and the defects in design or owing to decay should be noted there.

Temporary and semi-temporary roofing materials, such as corrugated iron or pressed asbestos tiles, should only be used to protect old buildings from the penetration of rain for a time, pending proper repair; and in these cases the old roofing materials, if of a permanent nature, should be stored for re-use as occasion offers. They should not be sold.

It is unnecessary to describe how old roofs may be patched; this is an everyday work of all builders.

The Repair of Tiled Roofs

It was not the old custom to board the back of rafters under the tiles, but sometimes modern use renders this desirable. Where this is done oak boards are to be preferred and these may be half an inch in thickness and need not be of like width. They may be laid butt-jointed or even with a slight space between them. When seen from below in conjunction with old timbers, boarding is more agreeable to look at if it is left from the saw or only partly planed. The modern practice of laying Willesden paper or thin ruberoid on the boarding is good, but where it is done ventilation must be provided between it and the tiles. A disadvantage of boarding below tiles is that when minor repairs are done the underside of tiling is inaccéssible, and it is convenient in such cases to be able to wire new tiles on to the battens or laths from below as they are pushed up into position from outside. A second disadvantage of boarding under tiles is that it becomes necessary to lay counter-battens beneath the tiling laths and these with the boarding raise the roof-level some two or two and a half inches, which may cause difficulties at the junction of the finished tiling with over-sailing courses against chimneys, gable ends or other walling.

Plain tiles were always hung with oak pegs on rent oak laths in old days; when soft wood began to be used in England fir and pine rent laths were used instead of oak and to-day it is the custom to use sawn deal tiling battens. In repairing the ancient roof of a monumental building it is best to follow the original practice and use rent oak tiling laths and oak pegs. These are seldom used to-day and there are consequently great variations in the prices quoted for them by the few firms who are willing to provide them. Seeing that they are more expensive than the trade article it is wise when ordering them to specify such lengths as can be used without waste. These laths should be about one and a quarter by three-eighths in section. The tiling lath is nailed either direct to the back of the rafters or to the counter-battens. When nailing rent lath to the rafters it is well to keep the nails in the lower half, for then if a lath splits the nail will still support the greater part of it. And as it is impossible to nail into them, tiles laid thereon must be hung with tiling pins or from nibs in the modern way. The best tiling pins are square oak specially split for the purpose. Composition and copper nails are also used for the purpose. Mr. Weir sometimes uses one oak and one copper pin on each tile.

There is much to be said in favour of hanging tiles without nailing them. It is the essence of a tiled roof that each tile shall be free to move a little to conform to movement in the timber roof due to climatic changes and to yield without breaking to gusts of wind. Indeed in the repair of old roofs this practice is probably the best, but it must always be accompanied by special precautions taken at the ridges, eaves and verges to enable tiling to resist at these salient parts the force of wind.

The practice followed in laying tiles varies considerably in different parts of the country. Nowadays tiles are usually laid dry; in old days they were often bedded in lime-and-hair mortar laid about an inch and a half along the tile head only. When tiles are thus bedded they should be allowed to stand in water before being laid. If no other provision is made to check driven snow, this practice followed by torching done from within is to be recommended. An old-fashioned practice sometimes adopted in the place of torching to prevent the entry of wind-driven snow and rain was to lay the tiling on second-crop hay. To serve a similar purpose I have found clean straw added some time after the roof was finished beneath the tiling lath between the rafters, laid in the manner of very light thatch. Mortar for torching should be "fat," tough, and should have plenty of tough long hair mixed with it.

Eaves, Verges, etc.

For structural reasons and to resist wind the edges of three courses of tile should show at the eaves. At the Philips Memorial at Godalming, designed by Mr. Thackeray Turner, four courses of tiles show at the eaves. They give a delightful appearance. The third course laid as a "stretching" course may be bedded immediately on the tilting fillet to give proper side-lap. This course and that resting immediately on it should be nailed down and fully bedded in mortar. The under-cloak, the lowest course, is best laid with the concave side upward, and this also applies to the bottom course of the verges, the edges of tiling showing at gable ends. The outer tiles of this part of a roof usually overhang the wall three or four inches, are secured with nails and are bedded solid with the edge pointed flush. A third or bottom course is used here also to give the outer tiles a slight tilt above the rest of the roof. They also make an even off it to the projecting verge.

In some parts of the country in the eighteenth century fired tiles were put in the place of stone tiles for roofing, but the tilted eaves are still covered with the latter. There is practical reason for this; but even were that not so, such treatment of the eaves deserves to be perpetuated for the sake of its beauty and the interest attaching to it.

The treatment of ridges, hips and valleys is a matter of considerable importance in the repair of roofs. The subject is well covered in many books on building construction; here it is sufficient to advise that photographs be taken of what exists as the roof is being stripped and that the old methods be followed again when the roof is re-covered.

Excellent photographs of a modern way of forming "swept" or "interlacing" valleys accompany Mr. Nathaniel Lloyd's paper on the subject which appeared in *The Brick Builder* of November 1926.

In the Middle Ages ridge tiles were sometimes modelled, but genuine examples of this kind are becoming rare. I have seen some on garden walls in Winchester, at Cleeve Abbey in Somerset (see Fig. 32,N), on the ridge of the church tower roof at Holnest (see Fig. 32,O), at the town cellars at Poole, and elsewhere. Where they are found they should be carefully preserved and sketches of them kept with the survey papers. The "ornamental" ridge tiles of the nineteenth century are, however, often disfiguring, though these seem to have taken forms inspired by those used of old. As a rule it is well to replace these new "ornamental" ridge tiles with tiles known among tile-makers as "half-round," though a flatter curve is more suitable.

The way in which the junction of tiled roofs with vertical walls is made is a matter of importance, both because it is at these points that rain often enters and also because the modern method of using lead flashing is conspicuously different from the old. In old days these joints were usually made without

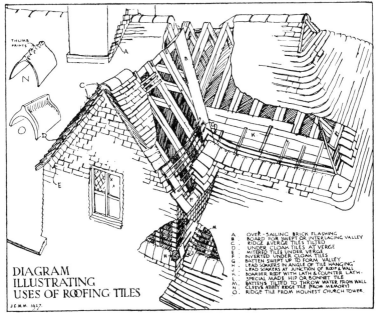

DIAGRAM
ILLUSTRATING
USES OF ROOFING TILES

J.E.M.M. 1927.

A : OVER-SAILING BRICK FLASHING
B : BOARD FOR SWEPT OR INTERLACING VALLEY
C : RIDGE ¿VERGE TILES TILTED
D : UNDER CLOAK TILES AT VERGE
E : MITERED TILES UNDER VERGE
F : INVERTED UNDER CLOAK TILES
G : BATTEN SWEPT UP TO FORM VALLEY
H : LEAD SOAKERS IN ANGLE OF TILE HANGING
J : LEAD SOAKERS AT JUNCTION OF ROOF & WALL
K : BOARDER ROOF WITH LATH & COUNTER LATH.
L : COUNTER LATH.
M : SPECIAL MADE HIP OR BONNET TILE
N : BATTENS TILTED TO THROW WATER FROM WALL
O : CLEEVE ABBEY RIDGE TILE (FROM MEMORY)
    RIDGE TILE FROM HOLNEST CHURCH TOWER.

THUMB PRINTS

FIG. 32

lead, the tiling being tucked beneath a projecting course of stone or brick and the space between being pointed with mortar. A further practical refinement was the custom of giving the tiling a slight tilt up against such walls so as to lead the rain away from the weak point on to the roof. In relaying a roof this tilt should again be given, but in addition to the protection given by an over-sailing course lead "soakers" without "flashings" may be used. I remember on one occasion cutting a chase at the direction of Mr. William Weir for roof tiling in the face of the wall of a circular tower.

The repair of tiling hung on a vertical face is governed by the same considerations as is the repair of sloping roofs, the lap, however, may be less and then more of each tile shows; also, tiling in this position is better nailed. In old work the junction between the vertical tiling in a gable and the verges of the roof is often made in the manner shown in Fig. 32 at E. This figure shows a variety of points in a plain tiled roof.

Pan-tiles

Pan-tiles are large tiles formed with an S-shaped section. They differ from plain tiles in that the side and end lap is obtained by the overlay of each tile on the adjoining and not by the overlap of each alternate course.

A pan-tiled roof is lighter than one of plain or stone tiles. These tiles, also, are laid to a lower pitch than are plain tiles, though in this the custom varies considerably. In Norfolk, for instance, the pitch is often that of thatch, indeed it may be that these tiles have often taken the place of that roof covering. Unless pan-tiles are laid by men used to the work it is difficult to make a sound roof with them. It is the nature of pan-tiles that they are so made as to fit one another. In the repair of an old roof it is not uncommon to find that all the stripped tiles are not quite of the same shape and therefore do not fit. Further, it is not uncommon that a number of new tiles are required. Great care should be taken to sort the tiles into sets of like kind and to use these together. It may be possible to use all the old tiles of like kind on one slope, and those of another kind, whether they are new or other old ones, on another slope. It is, further, well that a store of tiles should be kept for repairs and that these be clearly marked for the slope to which they belong. The manner in which pan-tiles are laid varies in different parts of the country; they may be laid dry or bedded with mortar on stout sawn tiling battens. There were traditional ways of finishing the ridges, eaves, hips, valleys and verges which have recently received close study and are described in textbooks on the subject. The small experience I have had with pan-tiles leads me to advise that the rafters be boarded, counter-battened, and covered with thin ruberoid or other like waterproof material and that the pan-tiles be laid above this on battens. Mr. William Weir writes that torching, which he says is important, cannot be done if the roof is boarded.   57

Stone Tiles

The method of laying stone tiles also varies considerably in different parts of the country. It seems that the wisest course is to follow the local tradition, checking it by a close examination of old roofs of similar material found in the neighbourhood. Indeed no better advice can be given with regard to the various slates in use. The very beautiful small slates of Devonshire deserve special attention, for the use of this material has not yet been revived, even by the devotees of local materials. The character of a building depends so much on the roofing materials that on no account should they be changed, and of all materials these small Devonshire slates are particularly delightful.

Thatch

Thatch is a neglected roof covering. In country districts the trade is still practised, but at a disadvantage, for the "reed straw" necessary for good thatching is difficult to get. Thatch has dropped out of use on this account rather than for any other reason, for the straw usually used has been bruised by the binder and in the thrashing machine, and as a consequence thatch has but half the life it had. The first matter of importance, then, in re-thatching an old building is to make arrangements during harvest time for enough wheat or rye to be cut in the old way and to see that the corn is withdrawn from the ear without passing the straw through a thrashing machine. Having got good "reed" the local thatcher needs little supervision, and his methods, again, vary in different counties. In Dorset the gables usually droop and are ended

in low hipped hoods.   In Suffolk the gable end is cocked up
and very occasionally is still decorated with a peacock or other
bird made in straw.   A well-thatched roof can be recognised
by the fact that little but the ends of the straw show and no

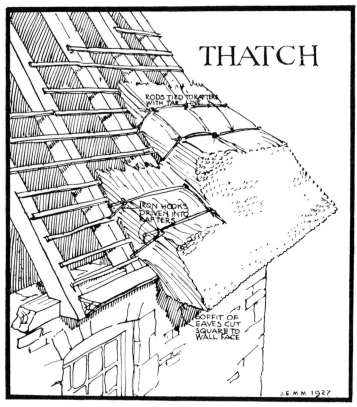

THATCH

RODS TIED TO RAFTERS
WITH TAR LINE.

IRON HOOKS
DRIVEN INTO
RAFTERS

SOFFIT OF
EAVES CUT
SQUARE TO
WALL FACE

J.E M M 1927

FIG. 33

straggly or bruised straws are to be seen at all.   In Norfolk,
some churches are still thatched, and the underside is visible
between the rafters of the open roof.   In this county riverside reed known as "Norfolk reed" is usually used; it is more
lasting than "straw reed" and therefore better.   At Ramworth
Church Mr. William Weir repaired the chancel roof beautifully

and followed the old custom of laying an interlacing basket-work of reeds immediately on the rafters which is seen from below and looks delightful. It is just such fine finish that makes an art of a trade.

A sketch of thatch being laid is reproduced in illustration of the following quotations from the letters of thatchers (see Fig. 33).

Mr. Fooks, of Stoborough Wareham, Dorset, writes: "I consider seventy-five per cent of the width of a building would make a good pitch for thatch." This gives an angle only a little under 60°. He adds however: "Not less than sixty per cent of the width of the house," which is about $52\frac{1}{2}°$. In continuation he says that the individual straws should "not be laid at less than 25°." "The straw is put on loose and pushed tightly together. The bottom layer or eaves is fastened by a rod and iron crooks about nine inches long driven into the wall plate. The remaining layers up to the top are fastened down by rods, and tied with tar twine, known in the trade as 'ropeyyarn,' to the battens or laths." "The thatch is well raked out with a rake (for the purpose) and trimmed off evenly with a hook known as a thatching hook (made only for that purpose)."

Mr. T. E. Cowell of Soham, Cambridgeshire, wrote that in finished thatch "the stub end, and a small piece, less than four inches, of each straw is seen." "Wood is the best tilt fillet, standing $4\frac{1}{2}$ inches above the rafters." For this purpose, bundles of straw laid level along the eaves "were used in very old work but not so to-day." "The first course is fixed with iron hooks, for it is not possible to bind it so tight otherwise." The other courses are held in position with hazel sticks or rods tied down to the battens with tar line. "The straw must have plenty of water thrown over it and then be combed out."

Messrs. Farman Brothers of Salhouse, Norfolk: "We finish the apex with rushes as Norfolk reeds are too stiff to bend over the ridge." "The hazel sticks are fastened about sixteen inches from the stub end of the reeds and are covered up with the next layer of reeds and are therefore not seen after the roof is completed." "We lay Norfolk reed the same length as grown. In Sussex we should have to cut them as they are very long and crooked."

Thatch is often laid on ash or other saplings instead of battens.

The construction of a roof designed for thatch is sometimes different from that for other coverings. The famous barn at Abbotsbury is an early example of this. There are no true principal trusses in this building and no true common rafters. Instead, there are fine strong collar couple-rafter trusses set (if I remember right) about five feet apart, and across them are set such saplings as are mentioned above, and on these the thatch is laid. This type of roof may be described as a "purlin," as opposed to a "rafter" roof. I do not know another medieval roof where this construction exists. If other examples of the kind are known to my readers, I would like to hear of them. It is clear from this, from the original design both of the masonry of this barn and from the form of St. Catherine's Chapel in the same parish, that the master builder who designed these was a man of outstanding worth, originality, and common sense. The isolation of this village, alone can account for the fact that his influence is not seen elsewhere.

Where heather is used for thatch on an ancient building, the practice should be continued.

Lead-covered Roofs

There is little medieval lead left on roofs in England to-day. Much of the spire on Ashwell Church tower (c. 1400), however, is still covered with the original lead, and one comes on porches or tower turrets still covered with it. Most of the leadwork on church roofs was cast and relaid in the eighteenth and early nineteenth centuries and has since been renewed or is in bad order. Until the middle and end of the nineteenth century cast lead was always used for this roofing and it was laid with hollow rolls. Lead laid in the eighteenth century and at the beginning of the nineteenth was laid in very long and wide sheets, and has suffered unduly as a consequence from excessive contraction and expansion resulting from changes of temperature. Such evidence as I know shows that the medieval plumber used narrow and short sheets of lead and cast it to a greater weight than has been done since.

Defects in lead roofs show themselves quickly. They have two origins—bad design and damage. Defects due to bad design include the use of large sheets of too shallow drips and poor fixing. Defects due to damage derive from the custom of cutting names and the pattern of feet on the surface. In the repair of leaks in a lead roof burning is to be preferred to the use of solder, though burning is seldom done now. 59

In deciding whether the lead on a roof should be condemned three matters will be considered: (1) Really old lead is valuable as an example of a medieval craft of which very little remains. It should be the aim of those in charge to repair and not to renew medieval lead. (2) The value of the roof covered by the lead and the probability of constant attention being given to the lead covering, also has weight in the decision. Properly cared for leadwork will endure for very long. If the chances are that it will be neglected it may be well for the sake of the roof below to have it up and to recast it even before it is fully worn out. (3) If the lead itself shows signs of much repair or has worn thin and is pin-holed it should be taken up.

When a lead roof is to be relaid on a noble ancient building it should be recast and not exchanged for new milled lead. Architects accustomed to using cast lead say that it lasts longer than the milled variety. Among these are Mr. F. W. Troup and Mr. William Weir. It is better in appearance and its use ensures the continuance of the traditional methods, which is so desirable in dealing with an ancient building. Recast old lead is stiffer to work than milled, partly on account of its nature and partly because it contains a small quantity of other metals as, for instance, silver. These "impurities" are never present in such quantity as to increase the value of the lead as old material. When it is decided to recast old lead it may be done on the site, either in the building under-going repair, in a temporary shed or in a building near by. In this way carting is saved and the work proceeds more expeditiously. There still remains at Northampton on the roof of the parish church a copper and low chimney built in a tem-porary manner against the tower. This was left there by the lead-casters of the early nineteenth century. When recasting is done all the solder should be cut out and virgin pig lead should be added in sufficient proportion to make the molten lead "run" easily on the sand-table. For general roof covering lead should not be recast to less than seven and a half pounds per square foot. It should be cut into sheets not longer than eight feet and not wider than two feet nine inches; this gives a finished width between rolls of two feet three inches. Lead will decay quickly if laid on new oak or cement; therefore the new board-ing immediately beneath it should be deal. The medieval builders used to lay it on oak slats about three or four inches wide with a space of an inch or even two between; and the lead lasted well, whether because of the ventilation or because the oak boarding was water-seasoned, which is the more probable 60 I do not know. The lead covering of roofs left unceiled may be still seen from below between the boarding in some churches, but as restoration and repair go on this becomes more and more rare, which seems a pity. The reason for changing this system is that such roofs are cold in winter and condensation beneath the lead occurs in changes of weather and drops of water fall to the floor. The fact that the "tingles" (described later) could be bent round the slats and fixed in position from below, a practice which holds the lead in position more securely than by nailing tingles on the surface of the boarding, was an advantage which the medieval builder made full use of.

It is Mr. William Weir's practice to lay oak boarding on the rafters as was done by the original builders and he is careful to re-use all that is left of the old, even pieces that are only long enough to stretch from rafter to rafter. On this he lays rough deal boarding, butt-jointed, and on that the lead. He specifies flat-headed wrought iron nails such as were used by the old builders for securing the sheets. Copper nails draw more easily from the boarding under the pull of the lead, though they have the advantage of being free from a tendency to rust. This advantage seems more theoretical than real, for I have never found the old wrought-iron nails rusted through.

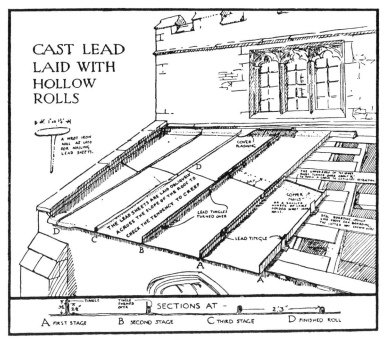

FIG. 34

When they have failed it is because the lead has torn away from them owing to creep. The lead sheets are further held in position by tingles, or pieces of lead about two and a half or three inches wide and nine inches long, nailed to the boarding and rising up between the upturned edges of the sheets, being bent over the edge of the inner sheet and fitted into a notch cut for the purpose there. (See Fig. 34.)

Lead gutters behind parapet walls are commonly found to be laid with drips of insufficient rise and where the gutters are long the drip from the roof to the gutter at its highest point is also often almost non-existent. Where this is so the gutter should be reconstructed so that no drip has a less rise than two and a half inches and no sheet a greater length than eight feet. The cesspits where they occur at the top of the down-pipes or shoots.should be at least four inches deep. Because of the rise needed to provide good drips and adequate fall in each sheet it may be found difficult to arrange for a proper lead gutter. In such cases and where the wall tops are wide enough, gutters made in concrete and covered with asphalt are a good substitute. The concrete bed that is used to form such a gutter may also be reinforced and thus will become a strengthening beam along the wall top. Some architects, among them Mr. Thackeray Turner, recommend asphalt in the place of lead on old roofs which are out of sight and when little money is available. I think there is risk of failure in laying asphalt on timber roofs and, for a monumental building, only recommend it when it can be laid on a solid concrete bed. Further, it appears to me a mistake to change the original structural design of an old building so drastically. Also it should be remembered that lead at seven and a half pounds per foot makes a lighter roof covering than asphalt laid three-quarter inch thick, or for that matter than any other roofing fit for a fine building, except copper. Asphalt laid in two layers to a total thickness of three-quarter inch weighs nine pounds per foot super. When asphalt is laid on an old roof the same practice as is used for the best modern work should be followed.

A point of weakness in a lead roof of flattish pitch is the lap between the head of one sheet and the foot of another. Water will travel up between sheets of lead as much as eighteen inches in such places. To check this the head of the undersheet should be turned over an inch or so and dressed down above the nail-heads. This will form an air pocket big enough to check capillary attraction.

Where roofs are steep the lead sheets may be laid with a slight rake, getting added support from one another and thus lessening the risk of single sheets creeping. It is customary where horizontal laps occur in a roof to "stagger" them, that is, to have each lap rather higher or lower on the slope than those on either side. In ridge roofs sheets of lead as long as fourteen feet may be laid right over the ridge and hang eight feet down one slope and six feet down the other.

The steeper the roof the smaller should be the individual sheets, and on spires the plumber of the Middle Ages devised a beautiful arrangement of sheets in herring-bone pattern which very much helps to resist the tendency each sheet has to slip downward.

Sometimes it is possible to repair a leaded roof by taking up the sheets, redressing them, perhaps at the same time reducing their size, and relaying them.

Cast ornaments and names found on old sheets should be preserved either in the building or burned into the new sheets of lead. It is desirable always to date the recast lead on a roof.

Copper Roofs

Copper roofs are very good, and as the material is sometimes cheaper than lead, and is very durable, it may be considered when re-covering roofs where lead has been used. But it must be remembered that copper is not a material used by long tradition in England for roofing, and although the green of old copper is beautiful in itself, the colour and the softer lines of lead are equally if not more beautiful. The copper roof of the north transept of York Minster looks hard and foreign as compared with the mellowed roofs of other parts of that building. 61

THE EIGHTH CHAPTER

CHURCH BELLS AND BELL-HANGING

There has been an increasing trade in the rehanging of church bells during the last thirty years, and during that time fine old bell cages which could have been repaired have been destroyed and replaced, old bells have been mutilated by the removal of their canons, and others—rare works of the sixteenth and earlier centuries—have been melted down. It seems therefore well to add a chapter on this subject.

A number of words are used in special senses in this craft and for that reason the more common are here explained and a sketch of a bell (Fig. 35) is reproduced with the various parts named.

The Parts of a Bell and its Fittings

The framework in which bells are hung is indifferently known as the carriage, the cage, or the bell frame. The top of a bell is fixed to stout blocks of elm as long or a little longer than the diameter of the mouth of the bell. These timbers are known as headstocks. The bell is fixed tightly to the headstock by iron straps and bolts passing through the group of staples known as the canon. The canon is cast in one piece with the bell. Nowadays the canon is sometimes cut off the crown of an old bell which is then drilled and hung direct to the headstock with bolts. This practice should be forbidden, for it has serious disadvantages, and these are not compensated for by the fact that the centre of gravity of the bell is thus brought nearer to the centre of oscillation. The old way of achieving this object is adequate; it was to *tuck* the canon *up* into the headstock by cutting a deep concavity almost equal to the height of the canon into it, so that the bell could be held in position there. When this is done care should be taken to keep the crown clear of the headstock so that the true ring of the bell may not be marred. Some bell-hangers, however, make their headstocks of cast iron and then it is difficult to

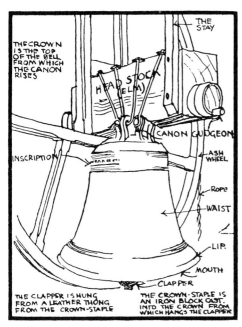

THE CROWN IS THE TOP OF THE BELL FROM WHICH THE CANON RISES

THE STAY

HEAD STOCK (ELM)

CANON GUDGEON

INSCRIPTION

ASH WHEEL

ROPE

WAIST

LIP

MOUTH

CLAPPER

THE CLAPPER IS HUNG FROM A LEATHER THONG FROM THE CROWN-STAPLE

THE CROWN-STAPLE IS AN IRON BLOCK CAST INTO THE CROWN FROM WHICH HANGS THE CLAPPER

FIG. 35

hang an old bell complete with its canon. Unless the canon can be used for the purpose for which it was cast, an iron headstock should not be used with old bells that possess these features. In the case of a new bell the matter is different, for they are cast with specially formed crowns, suitable for being bolted to the headstocks, whether these are of elm or of cast iron. The removal of the canon spoils the original form of the bell and also creates an additional risk of cracking the crown by putting a strain on it which it was not designed to take. The bearings in which the gudgeons turn used to be made of gunmetal cast in a dovetail shape, and let into the head of the side-wall of the bell pit. They are now usually cast-iron boxes with special ball-bearings within. The bearings are fixed to the heads of the frame on either side of each individual bell pit. The bell rope is attached near the top of the wheel which in its turn is fixed at one end of the headstock. At the other end of the headstock is fixed the stay; this stay strikes against and is steadied by the slider as the bell turns mouth upward during ringing. The slider is pinned below the wheel to the sill of the bell frame and is often shaped with a double curve so that it may clear the clapper and also rise to meet the stay. The clapper is hung by a leather thong to the crown-staple, and the latter is a piece of iron cast into the bell at its making. The fact that it is of different metal from the rest of the bell, sometimes causes incipient cracks in the bell crown when the casting is cooling. The crowns of bells should, therefore, be carefully examined by the surveyor to find if such cracks have developed.

When bells have been rung for many years the places where the clapper strikes become worn. When it is badly worn the bell should be "quarter turned," that is, it should be turned one-quarter round at the headstock and there be refixed. This ensures that the clapper will strike on a part of the bell mouth that is unworn. Some bell-hangers make difficulty about the fixing of the headstock to the canon in this new position, but such difficulties as exist can be overcome if skill is shown. When a bell has been quarter turned and has again become worn in that position it may be turned one-eighth, and so on.

Bell Cages.   New and Old Methods

In the old days bell cages were always framed of heavy oak timbers, but now often cast iron, steel or wrought iron are used instead. Recently teak and other hard and heavy woods have also been successfully used. Properly designed cages of either timber, steel or iron are equally good in an old tower from the structural point of view. Timber is more durable than steel and in a mediaeval or old tower is also more seemly.

The earlier bell cages were often over six feet high from the top of the head to the bottom of the sill. Later cages are usually lower, and now an oak cage is made as low as possible. The older cages were commonly made with heavy upright posts immediately below the bearings and with lighter ones at the corners of the cage or at the ends of the pits. These posts were braced or cross-braced.   More recent and modern timber cages are made without any upright posts, for there is a tendency for the cage to "ride" on the posts owing to the greater shrinkage in the braces of the grain of the wood at the shoulders.   It has been found that if all the bracing struts are set at one angle the shrinkage at their shoulders is all alike and the cage is steady.   The timbers of old bell cages were enormous; in the nineteenth century many were made far too light and still a new timber cage tends to err in this way. Some hold that the sound of bells is better when they are hung in a timber cage than when hung in one of iron.   I think this opinion is sound but the proof is wellnigh impossible.   In a medieval tower a timber cage is more seemly than an iron one; and the life of an iron cage is uncertain, whereas an oak cage will last for centuries if it receives proper attention.   A properly designed cage will ensure that the horizontal forces set up by ringing the bells will largely be nullified.   In a properly constructed cage the movement of one bell will be resisted by the whole cage, and not more by the parts adjoining than by others farther from it.   The cage should be set clear of the tower walls and should be carried by and bolted to crossed foundation beams, the ends of which should bear in all four walls, so that the weight and forces of the swinging bells may be met by the whole tower simultaneously and not by any two walls only.   The foundation of a bell cage, though the cage is bolted to it, should be an independent structure.   If a bell cage is not well designed it is likely seriously to damage an ancient tower, and this is particularly the case when an old post cage has been neglected and is wedged from the walls of a tower.   If a cage is not in good order with all the joints tight, the bells should only be chimed and not rung until it is repaired.

A Warning to Those Responsible for Old Bells

Because the public and Parochial Church Councils lack knowledge of bell-hanging and because bell-hangers do not value either old bells or old cages as they should be valued, many cages have been destroyed when they could have been preserved to fulfil their purpose for decades and many bells have been melted or mutilated when they might have been continued in use for centuries. It therefore behoves those who are responsible, to consider fully all aspects of the case before permitting changes to be made. The Society for the Protection of Ancient Buildings is always willing to advise on such questions.

There is additional cause why bell-hanging is not done as well to-day as it might be, unless special care is taken. There are not many firms of bell-hangers, and the subject is one full of technicalities little understood by the public. It usually happens that those responsible invite tenders from bell-hanging firms and as they do not tender from the same specification it often comes about that that firm which cuts the margin of safety finest or which has least regard for the strength of a tower, as apart from the bell cage, gives the lowest price and as a consequence gets the order. When competitive prices are desired, specifications and plans should be prepared from which the bell-hanging firms may tender on the same basis, so that their prices may be compared fairly. Thus only can the temptation to cut material be met.

The Survey of a Bell Cage

The survey of a bell cage is a prolonged and awkward job, for every joint and member should be examined. Those responsible for a ring of bells when they wish for a survey should be prepared to have the belfry thoroughly cleared out and the dirt around each beam cleaned away. Indeed, it is important that the guardians of a belfry should arrange for an annual cleaning, when the cage and bells should also be examined. Further, where the foundation beams are of oak the ends of each, where they are in the wall, must be seen before the surveyor can be certain that they are sound, and for this purpose the walling at one side at least of each beam-end must be withdrawn. When a survey of a cage is being made the ringers should be assembled and the bells rung and the movement between the cage and the walls carefully measured and recorded. This should be done before the walling is opened to make the examination of the foundation beam ends.

The calculation of the forces set up by ringing bells is a complicated matter and few are able to do this work; yet it is important, for such a slight change as the moving of a bell rope from one side to the other of a bell wheel may be enough to reduce the sway of a tower by thirty per cent. Mr. Edwin Lewis of the Green, Wishaw, Glasgow, by advising this change at Donhead St. Mary in Wiltshire was able so to improve matters that much building work was avoided.

As in other parts of an old building, the first aim should be to preserve the fine ancient craftsmanship that is connected with bells and bell-hanging as long as it can be made to do its work adequately, and the benefit of any doubt should always be added to the reasons for preservation. The second aim is to continue the use of the same constructive methods and of like-natured materials as in the original. A change in these should not be made unless it will prolong the life of the parts either adjoining, or as closely allied to the new work as is a tower to a bell cage.

Bells cast in the seventeenth and later centuries are usually dated; earlier bells can be told by the type of lettering on them, and very early bells are long and relatively narrow in the waist; also, as a general rule, the earlier a bell is, the taller will be the canon. Really early bells are usually without inscriptions.

Cracked bells have been successfully welded, but this process cannot yet be trusted to be invariably successful. The three common causes of cracks in bells are the expansion of the iron crown staple due to rusting, the cutting off of the canon and the consequent hanging of the bell by bolts through the crown, and a badly arranged chiming apparatus. The last fault occurs when the chiming hammer does not make a clean sharp blow, but hangs a while on the bell's surface, checking the sound vibrations in the bell itself.

The Treatment of Old Bells

Pre-Reformation bells, even when they are cracked or mutilated, should be kept, for they are rare works of art. Later bells should likewise be preserved if they are finely cast and of more than usually beautiful shape. Much harm has been done to old bells by retuning them. When this is reported to be necessary the matter should be fully understood before the bell is put in the bell-tuner's hands. In old bells the hum notes seldom accord with the tap note. Changes in the method of tuning are not of necessity an advantage. Many authorities prefer this irregularity of tone which some old bell-founders seem intentionally to have given their bells.

Always before a bell cage is repaired or renewed the tower in which it is should be known to be sound; therefore, with the bells and bell cage, the tower itself should always be surveyed and, if necessary, repaired.

The Society for the Protection of Ancient Buildings publishes a memorandum on bell-hanging which was drawn up at a joint meeting of members of the Central Council of Church Bell Ringers and of its committee.

In the explanation of the photograph (Fig. 36) of the interior of the belfry at East Bergholt, it may easily be seen that the bells are not hung for ringing, for there are no bell wheels. The canons have been cut from two of the bells that are seen in the photograph and these are supported from the headstock by bolts through the crowns of the bells. One bell on the extreme left of the picture—a modern bell—has a low angular canon which is a little "tucked up" into the headstock. The cage is an old one framed of oak in an unusual manner, one pit being set diagonally. The belfry, too, is unusual, not only because of the pretty grillage of oak which encloses it, but also because after the tower fell it was set on the ground under a low independent roof. When the photograph was taken the cage and belfry were in need of attention and repair.

FIG. 36. THE INTERIOR OF THE BELFRY AT EAST BERGHOLT

THE NINTH CHAPTER

THE REPAIR OF WINDOW GLAZING

Crown Glass

Before the nineteenth century most clear glass was crown glass. This is a kind made from blown glass spun at high speed until it spreads by centrifugal force to a large thin disk very slightly bellied. The centre of the disk is known as "bottle glass." But few of the "villas" of the first quarter of this century were without many sham or real pieces of bottle glass in windows and doors; in fact, so strong is the craze for a suggestion of the antique to-day that crown glass is now seldom made, except to obtain these centre pieces.

In earlier buildings crown glass was cut into diamond-shaped panes and set in leadwork; later it was cut into rectangles, which as time passed tended to become larger in size, until with the coming of sash windows quite large panes were glazed with this glass.

The late Mr. Sidney Barnsley suggested that diamond panes had their origin in an attempt to use this glass with complete economy. Glass being very expensive, every bit of the disk was of value, and the waste of any was probably held to be a mark of an incompetent glazier. By cutting a disk of glass into diamonds the minimum of waste is attained, for besides making best use of the disk itself, the corners and sides of a window light take the smaller scraps. Even the blurred centre (the bottle glass) was not thrown away, for it was used in the windows of attics and other unimportant rooms. It was not until glass became relatively cheap that people were able to afford the little waste that is occasioned by cutting the disk of crown glass into squares, and even then the resulting waste pieces were sometimes leaded in diamonds and put in the less important windows.

Owing to its very slightly bellied surface, crown glass glazing when seen outside a building catches and plays with the light shining on it most beautifully. For this reason crown glass should be preserved where it is found, whether in leaded panes in mullioned windows or in the larger sash frames of the seventeenth and eighteenth centuries. In the later sash windows this glass seldom has the lovely dimmed transparency which is sometimes present in older leaded lights, but it deserves respect none the less. Again, when repair work is in hand, and new glass is needed, crown glass is much to be preferred; but as it is more expensive than ordinary commercial sheet glass the latter may sometimes be substituted for it. In any case modern clouded glass should be kept out of old buildings, particularly that kind known as "cathedral glass." The latter glass disfigures many an old church window and where it has been inserted may be removed without scruple if clear crown glass is used in its place.

Leaded Panes

When an old window is to be glazed with leaded lights in the place of larger sheets of glass which have been substituted for the older form, it is good practice to set out the opening in rectangles and not in diamonds. New diamond panes have become so suggestive of the "mock antique" as to spoil the character of a window. When Sir Christopher Wren used leaded glass he divided the lights into rectangles.

When leaded glazing has become weak through age, it may sometimes be repaired without releading by turning back and re-cementing the flanges of the lead calms.

The widths of the leads chosen for the repair of old glazing is a matter deserving consideration, and in this the best guide is probably the size of the old calms. In the second half of the nineteenth century very thin leads were commonly used and in reaction to this practice architects have become accustomed to use very wide leads. Such medieval leading as remains in coloured glass windows is usually narrow and has a slightly rounded surface.

Leading is an especially important matter when ancient painted glass is being repaired. I would refer the reader to Mr. S. L. Brown's article on the subject which appeared in the April 1928 issue of the Journal of the British Society of the Master Glass Painters. The history of lead calms and the changes in their section which occurred as the centuries passed, is one of real interest. The medieval glaziers cast their calms and these were very narrow, but had stout webs. In the seventeenth century drawn milled calms were in general use, and then or in the eighteenth century the leaf was made slighter and was beaded on its rim. Most master glaziers use calms of such widths as actually suit best the pieces of glass that are being reset. The composition of the cement used for resetting old glass in the calms and the method by which it is inserted are both matters needing highly skilled technical knowledge beyond that of tradesmen only accustomed to make panels of modern glazing.

New Stained Glass in Old Buildings

During the Gothic revival an attempt was made to recapture the art of medieval stained glass painting. This attempt owed its origin to the recognition of the great beauty and richness of medieval coloured glass. The glass produced under this influence is already acquiring archæological value, and may in time find for itself admirers on other grounds. The present generation of the educated middle classes, however, holds this glass unpleasant and desires to be rid of it, and yet at the same time it continues the vain attempt to capture in newer glass the glory of the medieval craft. Its success is little if any greater than that of the preceding generation. That this statement is true may be tested by considering the comments that are made on new coloured glass in old buildings. There are a few who praise the work of a favourite stained-glass painter, a few definitely condemn, the majority declare the result to be only less intolerable than the work of the earlier trade-controlled revival. They say "It is not bad." It is nowhere received with unquestioned pleasure. It is probably impossible in an ancient building for a modern coloured window to be an improvement on old clear crown glass.

The Society for the Protection of Ancient Buildings advises that new stained glass windows should not be added to old buildings. That coloured glass was known to exist in olden times is a poor reason for attempting again to put it in a window. The late Mr. Micklethwaite heaped sarcasm on architects and clergy who made additions or alterations only on the ground that they were "correct." And William Morris, after attempting to adorn churches with glass of his design, held that old buildings were not the place in which to make such experiments. Indeed, they are too valuable. It seems only when the desire for stained glass is unconnected with archæological or ecclesiological learning that it is possibly justified; and, then, it is probable that such a desire will be best satisfied by setting panels of coloured glass in the clear glazing of an old window.

In the near future, it is not unlikely that many stained glass windows, painted during the Gothic revival, will be condemned, particularly where churches are darkened by a density of colour. That these old-fashioned windows form an interesting link in the history of glass painting has already been hinted. It is, then, perhaps the less surprising that I suggest here that, when the wave of destruction breaks, the central figure-work and the inscriptions should often be preserved, set in clear crown glass.

Although this book is concerned with the repair of ancient buildings, it seems, lest I should be supposed to condemn all glass painting, that the position must be further elaborated. Professor W. R. Lethaby has advised architects, craftsmen, and artists not to fear a spirit of adventure and invention in their work. And the use of new stained glass in modern buildings is as likely to be desirable as the product of any other art. To warn the public to shun such adventure in an old building in no way means that elsewhere it should not be encouraged.

Old Coloured Glass

Every scrap of old coloured glass should be most carefully preserved and this seldom in any other place than in the windows where it is found. Before repair is begun large-scale photographs and coloured drawings should be made of it, not only as permanent records, but also to ensure that when releading is done the old arrangement can be retained. It is not uncommon to find that the glass of an old window has been rearranged, if not mixed with glass taken from elsewhere. In such cases some may feel a conflict of desires, either to see the old glass of different designs separated and, as far as may be, releaded in its original relationship, or, alternatively, to preserve the accidental beauty derived from a confused display. And the latter desire will be reinforced by the knowledge that an attempt to re-establish order will bring with it problems much more difficult to solve than straightforward repair. Such groups of old glass have been assembled by our ancestors because no scheme, no design, was complete. When such a window is taken apart for reassembly in the original order many vacancies are found; and while the archæologist and the artist wish to have no make-believe restoration, the vacant spaces of clear glass breaking the unity of an old design are disagreeable to the ordinary man. While no rule can, or indeed should, be made in an attempt to cover the requirements of every case, it appears that in this matter, as in others relating to the maintenance of ancient buildings, the benefit of any doubt should be given to preserving such glass where it is found.

The Society for the Protection of Ancient Buildings makes three recommendations in general terms on the repair of ancient coloured glass. The first is that it should, if possible, be cleaned and repaired in position. This is more often practicable than is admitted, and should be attempted or at least carefully considered before removing the glass from its position. The second relates to glass that has to be taken from a window for repair, and is that the glass should not leave the building or the workshops attached thereto.   The third recommendation is with regard to those parts of an old window which are found to be missing. In this case the Society recommends that the completion of a window should on no account be attempted; that the missing spaces should be filled with pieces of glass, which may be toned a little so as not to confuse the relationship of the ancient work in the midst of which they are set.

In cleaning old glass preparatory to releading it, risk attends the use of hot or even warm water; and soda, or soap containing soda, should on no account be used.   Each fragment should be cleaned separately and only under the direct supervision of one who knows intimately the processes of painting and firing coloured glass.

When glass is being leaded it is the practice of some glaziers to smear the cement in a soft state all over the glazing and to work it under the leads by rubbing it in.   Thereafter they remove the cement that is left on the glass face by cleaning the glass surface.   It will be readily understood that this practice is very seldom desirable when valuable old glass is being treated.   In these circumstances it is almost always better practice to spread the cement under the flanges of the calms, which are then pressed down closely, care being taken the while' not to let the cement get on to the glass elsewhere.   The form of the calms to be used should be considered in regard to the method of cementing which is to be employed.

The Protection of Ancient Glass from Damage   63

When individual pieces of glass have become worn and frail they may be set between two clear pieces of thin new glass. This process is known as "plating."

With the preservation of ancient coloured glass its protection must be considered.   Mr. Thackeray Turner, who understands the value of ancient buildings as well as any living man, has said that no ancient glass, however beautiful, justifies the disfiguring wire or plate glass guards which are so commonly set on the outside of an ancient window. This extreme view may not accord with that of the majority of men and will not be accepted by those who set a greater value on glass than on the general seemliness of the building that contains it; but it has sound sense as a base, and it is only seldom that such protecting guards are in reality worth while. To use wire guards to protect modern glass in old windows is absurd, for modern glass can be replaced and its insurance is less costly than the provision of material protection. But as no money can re-create fine medieval glass, its protection in certain positions is desirable. No really satisfactory protective screen has yet been devised. Wiring, whether of copper or iron, is ugly, plate glass as ugly, and also, unless properly arranged to allow for ventilation between itself and the old glass, may become the cause of active decay in the latter. Further, unless such a protective screen is hinged or otherwise made easily movable, dirt collects on the backs of both new and old glass and cannot be cleaned off. It is possible that clear plate glass set in hinged gunmetal frames divided into rectangular panes, such as is used in fire-resisting doors in London offices, is the least disagreeable form of protection yet suggested, but it is not cheap.

It is a remarkable thing that dirt which would never be tolerated on glazing in houses, is allowed to collect and remain on the windows of churches. It is as desirable that old coloured glass should be cleaned periodically, as that any other work of art which deserves human care and respect should be so treated. But cleaning in such circumstances should only be entrusted to the control of a competent glazier, accustomed
64 to repair work, and aware of the value of the glass in his care.

THE TENTH CHAPTER

Common Defects

Ancient plaster ceilings were often simply, and sometimes richly, decorated with modelled or stamped ornament. In Mr. Laurence Turner's book on *The Decorative Plaster Work of Great Britain* there is an account of ways in which these ceilings were made in different periods. There is, therefore, no need to describe this here.

A plaster ceiling is laid on to laths which are nailed on to the underside of ceiling joists. Failure is usually due to one of three causes: (1) The rusting of the lathing nails; (2) the decay of the laths; or (3) the breaking of the plaster "key." The "key" is the plaster which was pressed between the laths when the first layer of plaster was applied, and which wraps itself over the laths, making the ceiling one piece with them. Of these causes the rusting of the nails is most common, the decay of the laths is not uncommon, but in old plaster the breaking of the key is almost unknown because hair of a very tough kind was used very generously, and also because the lime putty from which plaster is made used to be much more carefully slaked than it is to-day.

Propping an Old Ceiling

As soon as a valuable ancient ceiling shows signs of falling, it should be propped from below and great care should be taken not to damage the moulded ribs or modelled enrichments. Support should be given to the plain surfaces wherever this is enough. This may be done from planks, resting on upright and stayed props, laid an inch or two below all the projecting decoration. The immediate support beneath the ceiling should be in the nature of felt pads or strips on packing-pieces from the planking.

Examination from Above

When a ceiling is defective it should be examined from above, and as the backs of old ceilings are dust-laden, the first operation is to clean away all dirt.   This is tedious work if done by hand, because the back of the ceiling is by its nature very rough and because it is divided into so many compartments by the joists. Hand-cleaning is best done with soft-haired brushes such as are used by joiners in their bench work. But better and quicker for this purpose is a vacuum - cleaner. When the back of a ceiling is cleaned the causes and extent of failure can be fully estimated and the method of repair decided upon.

Methods of Repair

It may sometimes be possible to hold a ceiling in position by countersunk discs screwed to the joists, and to short new pieces fixed between them, as is described in the case of vertical pargeting. But the usual practice is to back the old lath and plaster with a reinforcement of new plaster strengthened with strips of canvas, the new work being fixed to the sides of the ceiling joists and to fillets of wood fixed between them. It occurs to me that fine copper wire mesh might be used instead 65 of canvas; it would have some advantages over that material, but I have never seen it used and cannot say that it would be successful. It is unnecessary to take down any part of an old ceiling to do repairs so long as it can be reached from the back.   The most difficult ceilings to maintain are those heavily moulded and modelled ceilings of the seventeenth and the first half of the eighteenth centuries. It may be found necessary to cut these or parts of them into sections and lower these sections for repair on the floor. Sometimes the bracketting, or curved timbers, which support a cornice or a cove has rotted, and must be renewed. When accessible these members may be strengthened in position by screwing on to them reinforcing pieces. Occasionally a whole ceiling must be carefully taken down, for some reason not closely connected with the repair or maintenance of the plaster-work itself, and when this is done the ceiling joists and bracketing should be renewed, wherever their durability is questioned; the plaster-work should then be gone over carefully and defects repaired before it is refixed in its original position. When a ceiling is taken down it is usually cut into manageable sections. It is, however, but seldom that an old ceiling cannot be repaired in position.

Renewal of Missing Features

Some ceilings to be repaired have already suffered from the loss of ornamental features; in such cases the debated question of restoration or strict repair arises. All are agreed that it is better to err on the side of doing too little reproduction than too much. Plaster ornament can be cast from moulds taken from the remaining original work or small patterns can be pressed on to the plaster while it is being laid on. The practice of reproduction in this way is held less reprehensible even by those who most strongly dislike "faked" or reproduced work than would be the renewal of work which depends for its beauty or interest on the personal cut or touch of the original work-man. The reason for this is that the new is reproduced in the same way and from the same models as was the old. It has, in fact, if it is well done, every quality of the old work except age itself. The reproduction of plaster decoration which was modelled in position by hand is, however, a much more doubtful practice.

Plasterer's Hair

I have found the cow hair sold for use in plaster to-day so poor as to be almost useless, and recommend the use of goat hair, which is both stronger and longer.

THE ELEVENTH CHAPTER

JOINERY

The repair of joinery is ruled by the same principles as control the repair of the larger timbers used in carpentry, but whereas in carpentry unseasoned timber may be used in some positions without harm to the work, in joinery all the wood used must be thoroughly seasoned. Again, in carpentry it is often fitting that the timbers should not be wrought, even when exposed to view, but in joinery a high finish is as desirable in repair as in new work.

Wall Panelling

Old panelling set against outside walls is particularly liable to rot, both from the action of fungus and from damp. In such positions it is first necessary to make sure that the wall is in a condition to withstand weather and that the causes of damp are removed, so that it may remain dry. Usually when panelling has to be repaired it should be removed from the wall and repairs done on the bench. When this is done the opportunity should be taken to point or plaster the wall face covered by the panelling and to dress it with picric acid or other germ-killing preparation. And before the panelling is refixed provision for ventilation at its back should be made. It may be advisable also to paint the back of the panelling with two or three coats of good lead paint. Such parts of the panelling as have to be repaired or made new to complete the whole need not always be so richly worked as the original. For instance, the Society for the Protection of Ancient Buildings would not recommend that new panels put in the place of others that were decorated should be worked as were the old. Missing panels of this type would be better replaced with plain panels. Again, where the styles and rails are richly moulded it may be well, if the seemliness of the whole is unaffected, that the new work should be of a simpler kind.

With increasing age, the archæological value of a work of art grows, whereas the value due to architectural form remains unaltered. Thus, a time comes when the restoration of missing parts, except on structural grounds, is undesirable. While it would be right to restore the missing fretwork of a late eighteenth-century architrave, the reproduction of the decorative pinnacled buttresses which were originally planted on a medieval door or pulpit should not be allowed. In the case of church screen-work and like finely carved works of joinery this is particularly so. "Before and after" photographs of the screen at Hanborough Church, Oxfordshire, which Mr. William Weir repaired are reproduced here in illustration of this point. 66 (See Figs. 37 and 38.)

It sometimes happens that the face of a decaying panel is beautifully carved or painted. In such cases what remains of the valuable face should be set on a new backing of dry seasoned wood of the same kind. This, if proper precautions are taken, may be done by planing down the back of the old to an even surface, thus removing much rotten wood. The thinned panel or the remaining pieces may then be strengthened from the back with a canvas glued on and then set on to a new panel. Sometimes the canvas strengthening may be dispensed with.

The Origin of Linenfold Panelling

Although it does not bear directly on the subject of this book, I should like to repeat here what the late Mr. Sidney Barnsley told me, as it is of considerable interest and has not, I believe, been printed elsewhere. He suggested that linenfold panelling had its origin in the following manner. Everyone knows that the beautiful display of silver grain in the panels of old oak was obtained because these panels were split

in planes radiating from the centre of the tree. When this
is done a series of wedge-shaped pieces of wood are made
as shown in Fig. 39, 1.

In preparing these pieces for panels it is necessary to plane
all the edges thin so that they may fit into the grooves of the
rails, styles and muntings.

This gives a panel with a slightly raised back as shown in

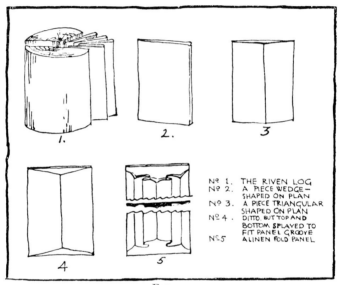

N° 1. THE RIVEN LOG
N° 2. A PIECE WEDGE-
SHAPED ON PLAN
N° 3. A PIECE TRIANGULAR
SHAPED ON PLAN
N° 4. DITTO, BUT TOP AND
BOTTOM SPLAYED TO
FIT PANEL GROOVE
N° 5 A LINEN FOLD PANEL

FIG. 39

Fig. 39, 2, where the back or raised face of the panel is seen.
Mr. Barnsley, who was unsurpassed as a carpenter, cabinet-
maker, and joiner, suggests that the craftsmen took pleasure
in the shaped back, and set the raised backs to show in the
place of the plane fronts. Further, he thought that to rib the
raised panel would suggest itself naturally to the mind of the
joiner. From this it is but a step to the fully developed
linenfold (Fig. 39, 5).

The reference to the late Mr. Sidney Barnsley turns my
mind to the consideration of his and Mr. Ernest Gimson's
attitude to the question of "Restoration."

FIG. 37.   HANBOROUGH CHURCH, OXON.   THE SCREEN BEFORE REPAIR
IN 1910

FIG. 38. HANBOROUGH CHURCH, OXON. THE SCREEN AFTER REPAIR
BY MR. WILLIAM WEIR IN 1911

If the ordinary layman, unable himself to use tools, realised that scholarly men like Mr. Ernest Gimson and Mr. Barnsley, who had added to their scholarship a skill in craftsmanship equal to any of former days and from a full knowledge of the subjects so acquired were keen adherents to the principles of the Society for the Protection of Ancient Buildings, refused to restore missing medieval features, he would surely hesitate before ordering that such attempts at "restoration" be made.

Paint on Panelling and Other Fittings

Much old joinery-work was coloured, and the colour, or traces of it, still sometimes remain. There are very few who will not agree that all traces of medieval painting, whether plain, patterned, or worked with figures, should be preserved without renewal. But one comes across painted decoration as late as the eighteenth century — marbled-work, graining, and flowers—which also deserves protection. It may be worth while to care for plain surface paint of that age, where it by chance remains, but most of it has been redone many times since.

English panelling of the fifteenth, sixteenth, and early seventeenth centuries was usually left its natural colour, though there is evidence that it was sometimes artificially darkened. Where old oak joinery retains its natural colour, a beautiful silver grey, it is well not to stain it or give it other surface treatment than can be done with a dry brush followed by the application of a little softened beeswax. Staining and oiling old oak, though a custom often followed to-day, is not to be recommended. In this respect also the treatment of joinery is like that of carpentry. Varnish also should not be used; this practice, once popular, has now almost disappeared.

In the eighteenth century it was a common practice to paint older panelling, just as the joinery made then was painted. To-day it is the fashion to remove the later paint, but this practice is by no means always wise. Paint does oak no harm but rather otherwise, and it never lessens the historic interest of old panelling; often also it makes a dark room lighter.

Further, with the removal of paint one is sometimes confronted with other difficulties. For instance, in a room which has been rearranged in the eighteenth century it may be that the newer modifications are of deal, and one is faced with the choice of substituting new work in the earlier manner and material for the later or with an emphasised contrast between the periods. In such a case it seems well to accept the changed treatment of the later period, paint and all. Panelling which has been painted again and again loses the keenness of the mouldings, but it acquires a mellowed softening which has a charm, if not a beauty, equally worth consideration.

The Removal of Paint and Varnish

Varnish was commonly applied to old unpainted panelling and other fittings in the nineteenth century and is now felt by almost everyone to be disagreeable. Mr. Noël Heaton has advised that it may be removed by using the following solvent: two parts of tetrachlorethane and one part of stearine. This forms a liquid which, brushed on the surface, softens the varnish after standing a few minutes, so that it can be rubbed off with a cloth or stiff brush, preferably dressed with a little very fine powder. On smooth surfaces a stripping knife could be used without ill effect. Only as much of the woodwork as can be stripped of paint in half an hour should be dealt with at a time, for the solvent evaporates and the varnish hardens again as it dries. Paint removers based on the above preparation may also be obtained and of these, "Pintoff" made by Holzappel and Co. and "Parvo" made by Polvar Ltd. are two.

THE TWELFTH CHAPTER

THE PROTECTION OF WALL PAINTINGS

Paintings are commonly found in the British Isles on
plastered wall surfaces in domestic and ecclesiastic buildings
down to the seventeenth century. In many cases these have
been hidden under a coat or coats of limewash, either because
they had become damaged or because they were no longer
thought fitting. At the present time those which are exposed
have as a rule been uncovered and there is no doubt that many
more still exist hidden below layers of limewash on old plaster.
On this account, wherever old plaster exists the walls should
be examined for wall paintings before any plaster is removed
and before any new decorative washes are applied. And a
record should be kept even if nothing is found.

It will be seen, then, that the treatment of wall paintings
comes under two heads—their uncovering and their protection
when uncovered.

How to Uncover Wall Paintings hidden by Limewash

The removal of the coats of limewash which hide old paintings should only be undertaken by a person experienced in the
work, or by someone appointed by him to work at his direction.
A knowledge of archæology is also required, as it is frequently
found that a wall has been redecorated with paintings in succes-
sive centuries, each picture being put on a fresh coat of limewash. In such cases it is necessary to know which is the most
valuable picture, and if possible, a photograph should be taken
of each painting as it is exposed. As a rule it will be found
that the painting directly on the original plaster is the best
preserved, and that the limewash ground of the later pictures

187

WARNING: PLEASE READ NOTES ON PAGE 213.

had peeled off in parts before the later repainting was done. The removal of the upper layers of limewash separately is sometimes very difficult. Where it is found that the more valuable painting cannot be uncovered without damage, the work should be discontinued; the wall is, then, better left to hold its secret till some more favoured generation can disclose it.

In another chapter I have referred to the medieval practice of plastering and limewashing the inside faces of walls. But it is not amiss here to restate that no old plaster should be removed, for fear of destroying painting upon it. The builders of old often carried the plaster round the wrought quoins of the inner window jambs, a thing which is never done now. Not uncommonly the painting continues round into the window cheeks, either laid on the plaster above the jamb stones or on limewash directly applied to these stones themselves. If, therefore, it is desired to preserve an old building intact, care should be taken, and modern custom should no more be allowed to rule a decision here than elsewhere.

The removal of the coats of limewash is accomplished in variety of ways, according to the condition of the wall. It should never be undertaken during building operations. In some cases limewash will flake away if gently lifted by a palette-knife lightly inserted below the outer skin. It is more usual, however, to find that this cannot be accomplished till the outer coat has been loosened by gentle taps from the wooden handle of the palette-knife. Sometimes it is necessary to press the edge of the knife gently on the very border of the covering limewash, and to flake off pieces no bigger than one-eighth or one-sixteenth of an inch with a gradual cutting movement. For this work a fine ivory or bone paper-knife has also been found useful. Professor W. E. Tristram writes that he has never found anything better for this work than a dinner-knife, sharpened moderately all round at the top. If any process is found to be marring the painting, another must be tried, and, possibly, it may be necessary to abandon the work altogether.

The removal of limewash from paintings is a most tedious

WARNING: PLEASE READ NOTES ON PAGE 213.

FIG. 40. WEST STOW HALL, SUFFOLK. A MURAL PAINTING

occupation. After working for an hour or two, one is apt to tire and unconsciously become careless. In that case work must be stopped until interest and energy have revived.

The surface of an old painting, when first exposed, is often dusty and the colours will rub off easily; even the light use of a camel-hair brush may be inadvisable. In such cases the dust may be blown off. A Fletcher's foot blower to the outlet of which has been fitted an indiarubber tube with a suitable nozzle is recommended for this purpose. For want of proper care paintings have been smudged. In a picture of which only part remains, any extra lines caused by careless handling are most confusing and sometimes impossible at a little distance to distinguish from the original. To avoid spoiling the painting during the work of uncovering, therefore, it is usually best to leave dusting till immediately before any fixative is put on.

The Protection of Wall Paintings

Wall paintings must be protected from the action of (1) damp, (2) soluble saline matters, and (3) sulphuric acid produced by combustion of coal and coke.

Of these three, the cure for damp walls has already been discussed in this book; and unless a wall is dry other precautions will be of no avail. Indeed, before an attempt is made to uncover a hidden painting, the wall on which it is must be made dry.

The soluble saline matters which are damaging are principally due to the burning of gas in a building and can only be prevented from collecting by the disuse of gas, though thorough ventilation will reduce the risk of any harm.

The fumes from coke and coal should not be allowed to enter the building, but should be led away in proper sealed flues.

When these causes of decay no longer exist the preservation
69 and protection of old paintings is simplified.

70 Fixing a Wall Painting

The surface being uncovered and the painting prepared to receive a fixative, the question of what to apply needs consider-

WARNING: PLEASE READ NOTES ON PAGE 213.

ation.   The condition of the wall and of the painting are the factors which rule the answer to this question.   Preparations which have been used are described below, but the results so far obtained from fixatives indicate that it is not always advisable to use them.   The author himself would never attempt to fix a wall painting without first consulting Professor W. E.. Tristram, whose work at Westminster Abbey has proved his opinion to be of the highest value.   A vegetable wax diluted in a volatile spirit and applied thinly appears to give the best results and to carry with it the fewest risks. White's Patent Spray Diffuser with a copper receiver is a suitable apparatus for the application of liquid preservatives. The spraying should only be repeated when the preceding sprinkling has dried.   Too lavish a spraying is bad for a painting; there is less danger in applying too little.   The liquid should rest on the wall like condensation and spraying should be discontinued when drops accumulate.   The operation should certainly be stopped when the surface shows a tendency to become shiny.

In cases where the wall is perfectly dry and free from saline matters, the following preparation has been used:

25 measured ounces of pure toluol:

100 grains of ceresin:

1 measured ounce of Winsor and Newton's Picture Copal Varnish.

When used, this mixture should be applied warm.   The preparation should be clear, and is the nearest approach to a varnish that it is ever permissible to employ.

Professor Tristram's comment on this preparation is valuable, so I add it: "The quantity of copal varnish suggested here I have observed is enough to discolour the painting.   Anyhow, it would become brittle in time and counteract the effect of the wax.   A spot of linseed oil, say, less than one per cent, is useful, as it prevents the wax blowing."

Where the colours and ground are firm, solutions may be applied with a broad flat brush.

WARNING: PLEASE READ NOTES ON PAGE 213.

It is sometimes advisable to make trial on a small portion of the painting, but as most solutions are not miscible with others, the apparatus and brushes used for one must not be used for another; and no part of a painting should be touched with different liquids.

Varnish, with rare exceptions, has proved disastrous to distemper paintings on plaster. One result of the varnish treatment is the confining within the porous substance of the plaster of air and other gases, and, with changing temperatures, these are apt to expand and lift both varnish and painting from the wall.

The Repair of the Plaster Background

There is one other point which should be mentioned in connection with paintings on plaster. When the limewash has been removed it is often the case that the old plaster exhibits a cracked and pitted surface. These flaws can be stopped with fine plaster which may be coloured with limewash to a tone similar to the ground of the picture, but this stopping needs special care, as the new plaster used should on no account smear over the edges of the cracks or pits on to adjoining surfaces. The old plaster should not be touched with new colour nor should any attempt be made to restore the picture in line or colour on the wall. It is interesting, however, to make restorations to full size or to scale on paper and if these are hung near a damaged or defective painting they help the amateur to realise the story of the picture.

Paintings on wood or canvas may sometimes need varnish, and then the best mastic varnish, not copal, should be used. The surface of the painting must be clean and dry before the application.

Protection by Glass

The attempt to protect wall paintings by glass covering is rarely to be recommended and, when attempted, the glass should be easily removable for cleaning.

WARNING: PLEASE READ NOTES ON PAGE 213.

A LAST NOTE

It is almost as difficult to know where to stop writing of the repair of ancient buildings as to know where to stop actually doing the work. Many more matters relating to the subject might be mentioned.

The heating of ancient buildings is a vexed question often bringing with it the troublesome business of siting the low-level heating chamber which may cause disturbance of adjoining foundations. Particularly difficult is this matter when churches are under consideration. Often in these buildings the old-fashioned use of stoves is more satisfactory than is the installation of a boiler, pipes, and radiators. Excellent recommendations in regard to the warming of churches will be found reprinted in Appendix I. These were drawn up by the Society for the Protection of Ancient Buildings.

The arrangement of bathrooms in old houses and the pipes that lead to and from them is difficult. As a rule the pipes should be within the house rather than set on the wall face outside.

Much also might be written on the subject of electric lighting, but I have thought it sufficient to reprint in Appendix II directions which are based on those issued by the Bath and Wells Diocesan Advisory Committee to the guardians of churches of that diocese. Although these were drawn up specially for churches they can be applied without much alteration to domestic and other buildings.

Additions to ancient buildings made necessary by changed conditions and new uses are a matter on which a great deal might be profitably said. One school claims that the new work should be modern in design and material. The Society for the Protection of Ancient Buildings holds that such work should be unobtrusive—as little noticeable as possible.

Consciously modern and consciously stylistic work cannot satisfy this requirement, and it would seem that, in the main, the building materials and methods should be like the old, and that an imitation of the ancient style should be avoided rather than pursued.

The surroundings of ancient buildings also deserve consideration; and it would seem that the wisest course is to keep them as clear of new structures—walls, railings or memorials—as may be. It is also probably wise, when trees are being planted in such places, that they be native to the country; and the same also may be said of flowering plants and shrubs.

On the whole, however, it will be seen that the best way to maintain an old building is to give it that constant attention, —"Daily Care" as William Morris wrote it—which most people give to the houses they live in. Large building operations of the wholesale nature which were common in the last half of the nineteenth century are much less likely to be so kind to ancient work as is periodical maintenance. In fact to do small repairs when they seem to be needed is the way in which an old building may best be maintained. Sometimes, it is true, bigger works are necessary, and it has been one of my objects in writing this book to show how these may be carried through without harm to a building.

And lastly, let me again remind the reader that an attempt to recover or expose original forms too often produces difficulties in regard to the replacing of missing features. This and the modern desire to carry through such attempts has led to much harm to examples of old craftsmanship. It gives those who enjoy genuine ancient workmanship uneasy doubts; and by contrast we all love unrestored cottages or churches. Indeed it was the dislike of the common results of wholesale restoration which fifty years ago impelled William Morris to form the Society for the Protection of Ancient Buildings.

APPENDIX I

HEATING BY STOVES

1. Where floors and walls are occupied by monuments and brasses of historic or sentimental value, it is generally inadvisable to heat an ancient church by a hot water system. The building of this form of apparatus requires trenches and usually wall space, also it is often accompanied by risk of damage to foundations.

2. (*a*) An excellent method of warming buildings is by the use of large gilled stoves (i.e. Gurney stoves) suitably placed.

(*b*) If possible these stoves should be placed so that the hot air rises from them to the highest part of the building, gradually warming and displacing the cold air collected under the roof.

(*c*) It is advisable to keep the stoves alight continuously during the winter months, so that the air in the building will get thoroughly warm, and then heat losses through walls, windows, and roofs can be made good with a less consumption of fuel.

(*d*) These stoves have the following advantages:

Small initial cost.

Little structural work to install.

Easily removed in the event of cheap electricity in the future making electrical heating possible.

3. The following recommendations should be observed in installing Gurney stoves or similar heating agents:

(*a*) Smoke pipes should be carried as high and as straight as possible and should be finished with adequate cone-caps to prevent rain and snow driving down the pipe.

(*b*) All bends should be fitted with cleaning doors of the same diameter as the pipe. These doors should be fitted with gunmetal studs and fly-nuts and made easily removable, but smoke-tight.

(*c*) Stoves should be supplied with heavy cast pedestals to take the weight of the smoke pipe and to make the heavy wrought-iron caulkings into the walls, etc. unnecessary; light balancing fixings only being required then.

(*d*) All joints in the smoke pipes should be securely and properly caulked with asbestos yarn and fire-resisting cement and made absolutely air-tight.

(*e*) All sockets inside the building should be fixed so that joints are caulked downwards from above to prevent the jointing falling out.

(*f*) All sockets outside the building should be fixed so that joints are caulked upwards from below to prevent rain, etc. percolating between the pipe and the socket.

(*g*) Smoke pipes passing through the roof should be fitted with heavy galvanised wrought-iron sleeves fitted with oblique flanges, the joint between the flue pipe and the sleeve should be packed with asbestos and made weather-tight. All woodwork should be kept well clear of this sleeve.

71 (*h*) Mr. William Weir recommends the use of "Everseal" paint, made and sold by the Anthracite Radiation Company Ltd., of 5 Newman Street, W.1, for painting flue pipes where they are exposed within a building.

(*i*) These stoves must be placed on a stone, concrete, or tile floor six inches thick, extending at least three feet in front of the stoking door and one foot three inches on the sides and back.

LOW PRESSURE HOT WATER APPARATUS

Where floors can be easily (i.e. without damaging tombs, etc.) excavated to form trenches, low pressure hot water heating apparatus, consisting of a boiler, radiators, and mains, run in trenches formed in the floors, can be installed without difficulty, providing the foundations of the building and the subsoil are suitable.

Boiler

This should be of cast sectional type with a large fire-pot and of ample heating surface to allow infrequent stoking and a slow consumption of fuel.

The following points should be observed:

(*a*) The boiler-room should be sunk so that the top of the boiler is at least eighteen inches below the floor line of the building.

(*b*) The smoke pipe of the boiler should be connected to a brick flue of

(1) *larger* area than the area of the smoke outlet, if *rectangular*;

(2) *equal* area to the area of the smoke outlet, if *circular*.

(*c*) The boiler-room may be some distance from the building, if required, but then ducts will be necessary in which to run the flow and return mains.

(*d*) The boiler and the mains outside the building should be insulated with non-conducting asbestos composition.

(*e*) The boiler should be fitted with a proper dead-weight safety valve, so arranged that it cannot be tampered with, and a draw-off cock; a thermometer to register the temperature of the water should be fixed either on the boiler or on one of the mains from it.

Radiators

1. Radiators should be of a cast-iron, screwed-nipple type with vertical sections of varying widths and heights to suit the requirements.

2. Each radiator should be fitted with controlling valve and air valve and be piped in such a manner that any one or any number can be shut off without affecting the others.

3. Radiators should, as far as possible, be so distributed that heat is emitted equally round the building.

4. If possible, some radiators should be fixed in the middle gangway, so as to prevent the cold air from descending in the centre of the building.

Mains

1. All mains in trenches should be of heavy cast-iron, with either caulked joints or patent Richardson rubber joints.

   (*a*) If caulked joints are used these should be made with best caulking yarn and red and white lead; cement should not be used.

   (*b*) The patent Richardson's joints should only be used where pipes are easily accessible.

2. Mains should be so graded that one circuit does not take preference over another, and so that the temperature of the water in all is equal.

3. Mains should be fixed on rollers and allowances should be made to ensure free expansion and contraction.

4. All mains should be properly vented at the highest point with pipes open to the air and the incline from and to the boiler should be the same.

5. An adequate expansion-tank of sufficient capacity to accommodate all water of expansion should be fixed at least five feet above the highest circulating point of the apparatus.

6. Heating by iron pipes in trenches under gratings is not advisable owing to the amount of organic matter which accumulates in

the trenches and gives off objectionable odours when the apparatus is working.

HIGH PRESSURE HOT WATER APPARATUS

A high pressure hot water system.is not recommended.

ELECTRIC HEATING

Electric heating will probably prove the best method of heating an ancient building, and it should be remembered that it may shortly be within the means of all.

APPENDIX II

72 **NOTES ON THE USE OF ELECTRICITY IN ANCIENT CHURCHES**

Regulations for Installation of Electric Light

1. The application for a faculty must be accompanied by a full specification, plans showing the positions of lighting points, switches, etc., and the name and address of the contractor.

2. The insurance company in which the church is insured against fire must be notified, and any directions that the company may issue must be complied with.

Generally

(*a*) Under only very exceptional circumstances may holes be made or drilled through buttresses and piers, and never through mullions, columns, detached shafts, or vaulting ribs.

(*b*) Beams, structural timbers, or mouldings are not to be notched or sawn on any surface. When it cannot be avoided, the smallest possible hole may be drilled through the centre (the neutral axis) of a beam.

(*c*) Wiring must not be laid over the surface of any carving or painting, nor must it be laid over the face of mouldings where another course is possible.

(*d*) Where woodwork, e.g. pews or panels, must be pierced, the smallest possible hole should be drilled carefully in the most inconspicuous position so as to avoid splitting out or mutilation.

(*e*) Wires should not be led along walls that are liable to damp, e.g. below the lines of valley gutters. If no other position is possible, the conduit or cables should be kept at least three-eighths of an inch clear of the surface by means of special spacing-saddles.

(*f*) As wiring deteriorates with lapse of time, the conduit or cables should be laid in such positions that they can be examined from time to time, and replaced when necessary.

(*g*) Ordinary wooden plugs must not be used except for wide mortar joints. Plugs of "Rawl," "Metlex" or similar type must be used for pluggings into stone, especially when dressed, keeping the hole as small as possible. For external work lead plugs must be used.

(*h*) All screws should preferably be of brass. Wire staples are not permissible.

Wiring

(*a*) The installation must comply with the latest edition of the regulations issued by the Institution of Electrical Engineers for the electrical equipment of buildings.

(*b*) Where steel conduits are used they should be either "solid drawn," "welded," or "brazed," either screwed or with a grip joint of approved make, and all main and sub-switches, fuses, distribution boards, ceiling roses, and wall plugs should be ironclad, giving full protection to the whole of the wiring from the supply authorities' terminals to the lighting points.

(*c*) The conduit system should be "earthed" to a rising water-main. Where this is not possible a tough rubber-sheathed cable system is to be preferred.

(*d*) Where a metal-sheathed system is employed, the metallic sheathing with ironclad switch gear, etc. is to be made mechanically and electrically continuous and is to be "earthed" as in the case of a conduit system.

(*e*) Where a tough rubber-sheathed cable system is employed, the cables, where liable to mechanical damage, are to be protected by hardwood or steel channels.

(*f*) Electroliers and hanging fittings are to be suspended by chains, tubes, or other means so that the electrical cables or flexible cords to the fittings are under no mechanical stress or strain.

(*g*) The contractor shall furnish the church authorities with a certificate signed by him setting out the tests for

(1) Insulation resistance of the installation complete with fittings.

(2) Actual resistance in ohms of the conduits or metal sheathing to "earth as measured from at least three points remote from the "earthing" point.

(*h*) Distribution boards are to be provided with circuit lists setting out

(1) The lighting points and total wattage controlled by each way.

(2) The material and gauge of the fuse wire to be used on each circuit.

This list is to be affixed either to, or adjacent to, the distribution board.

(*j*) Switches which are not fixed adjacent to the lights they control are to be suitably labelled.

(*k*) Particular attention is drawn to the regulations dealing with the following points:

(1) In the case of conduit systems, that no cables should be "drawn in" until the whole of the conduits with fittings are permanently fixed, also that the conduits should be of a sufficiently large size to allow of an easy draw "in" or "out."

(2) The identification of cables by colour or other suitable means.

(3) That the lamp leads are in all cases connected to the neutral or earthed pole of the supply system.

(*l*) It is desirable that schemes should be based upon definite illumination values required and defined and that the design, arrangement, and position of the fittings should be such as will eliminate all tendency to "glare."

Fittings

(*a*) Interesting or ancient candle sconces, standards, or chandeliers must not be removed without authority. As far as possible they should be retained in their original positions; sometimes they can be adapted for the electric light. Sham candles are an abomination.

(*b*) Light iron, and especially steel fittings, are not suitable for use in the open air, or even in porches, as they are liable to rust.

(*c*) When wooden blocks are used for mounting switches or apparatus they are to be of hardwood.

GLOSSARY

Abutment. A masonry or brick support to an arch or other structural member which exerts thrust towards it.

Anchor beam. Having reference to concrete foundations: a reinforced concrete beam placed to tie back foundations and so to prevent lateral movement, as would an anchor.

Arris. The sharp edge formed at the line where two planes meet.

Ashlar. Masonry built of smoothly wrought stone in courses.

Batten. A strip of wood, usually not more than $1'' \times 2''$.

Bottle glass. The centre nobble of a sheet of crown glass.

Bracing-piece. A timber framed diagonally into two other timbers which are framed together to an angle, to secure their relative positions; with them it makes a triangular structure. It may be in compression or tension.

Bracing-strut. As bracing-piece, but always in compression.

Brick-nogging. The brick-filling in a timber framed wall or partition, used chiefly in slight structures. In heavier oak framed walls such brickwork is usually called brick-filling.

Breeze. Finely crushed cinders, usually obtained from gas works.

Burning (of lead-work). The process of welding the edges of two sheets of lead together with heat.

Cage (of church bells). The open timber or metal framework in which bells are hung.

Canon. The group of loops cast with a bell at its crown by which the bell is hung.

Carpentry. The structural timber-work of a building.

Caulk, to. To stop seams between timbers with oakum and melted pitch.

Center or centre. The timber framing on which is supported an arch, a dome, or such-like structure during its erection or repair.

Cesspit (of lead gutters). The small sunk pit into which a gutter pours before its discharge into a rain-water head or shoot.

Chamfer. The shape of the angle of a squared timber when the arris has been cut off.

Chase. A long groove cut into a wall or a timber.

Cladding. Roof boarding.

Clay-lump. Lumps of clay, tempered with straw or reed and dried in the sun, usually about $6'' \times 9'' \times 1' \ 3''$.

Cob. The material of which mud or chalk walls are built. Wet clay or chalk is tempered by the tread of horses with straw or reed. It is lifted wet on to walls and there allowed to dry hard. Shrinkage is considerable. The surface is trimmed in position as it hardens. The surface is usually afterwards plastered or limewashed.

Collar. The timber which unites two opposite rafters or principal rafters at a distance above their feet.

Conduit (of electric wiring). A tube into which the wires are drawn for protection.

Counter-batten, to. To lay battens at right angles to, and beneath or above other battens.

Courses (of masonry or brickwork). The horizontal and level lines of either material. In a wall courses are laid one on the other.

Creeping (of lead). The tendency to slip down the slope of a roof due to expansion and contraction caused by temperature and the pull of gravity.

Crown (of a bell). The metal that forms the top of a bell.

Crown-staple (of a bell). The iron staple cast into the crown of a bell to take the clapper attachment.

Damp-proof course. A course of impervious material built into a stone or brick wall to prevent the rise or descent of moisture in the wall.

Delta metal. A copper alloy having great compressional and tensional strength and which is not subject to rust.

Dowel. A metal, slate, stone, wood, or other stout pin let into two adjoining materials to keep one from slipping on the other.

Drag. An implement for making smooth the face of a stone. It is a thin sheet of steel shaped as half a circle with saw teeth on the straight edge.

Drip (of plumbing). The low step between two sheets of lead in a gutter or on a flat. Drips are set at right angles to the direction of the " fall " of the gutter or roof.

Drift. The movement in masonry or framed structures due to expansion and contraction, usually caused by changes of temperature and the force of gravity. After each expansion gravity hinders a complete return to the original position. The movement in each case is infinitesimal, but being cumulative ultimately becomes serious.

Ears (of cast-iron rain-water pipes). The pieces of metal cast with the pipe by which it is attached to a wall.

Encaustic tiles. Tiles into the surface of which coloured and patterned clay has been fired. They are often highly glazed.

Entasis (of spires). The slight convex swelling of the facets and angles between the base and the apex.

False tenon. A tenon made of a piece of wood separate from the timber of which a tenon normally is part. It is let into and secured to that timber, and bears in all respects the same relationship to it as a real tenon except that it is not a true part of it.

Fillet. A small continuously squared member in a group of mouldings; a narrow strip of wood.

Flashing (of plumbing). The narrow strip of lead, tucked and secured into a wall and bent down to cover an upturned piece of lead so that rain running down the wall cannot enter between the lower sheet and the wall.

Flitch (of timber beams). A steel or iron plate inserted on edge down the middle of a beam and secured to the two sides.

Grout. A liquid mixture of cement and sand or of cement alone.

Gudgeon (of bells). A metal pivot set in the under side of the headstock of a bell on which the bell swings.

REPAIR OF ANCIENT BUILDINGS 202

Gudgeon-socket (of bells). The gunmetal bearings set in the side-heads of a bell-pit in which the gudgeon turns. To-day its place is usually taken by ball bearings.

Hammer-beam and hammer-beam roofs. A hammer-beam is the large horizontal timber on which the foot of a principal rafter of a hammer-beam roof rests. It projects from the wall about one-fourth or two-sevenths of the span of the roof. On its outer end stands the hammer-post which gives additional support to the principal rafter at a considerable height above the hammer-beam. In its turn the projecting end of the hammer-beam is supported by a curved bracing-strut springing from a wall-leg. The latter (the wall-leg) often rests on a corble, and at its head is tenoned into the under side of the hammer-beam. Collars usually join the principal rafters at the heads of the hammer-posts, and are themselves supported in the middle by curved bracing-pieces which spring from near the feet of the hammer-posts, and together make a complete arch.

Hardcore. Clean stone or brick broken to the size of large road metal.

Headstock (of bells). A heavy and deep piece of elm a little less in length than the width of a bell-pit. The bell is hung from it; the gudgeons are set in its under side; the wheel is fastened to one end of it. Thus with the rotation of the wheel it swings the bell.

Hip. The angle of a roof formed by the intersection of two slopes of a roof above the projecting corner of a building.

Holder bat. A ring-headed metal fastening set into a wall for the support of a rain-water pipe. The outer part of the ring, through which the pipe passes, is made to open or to be removed.

Jack. A contrivance by which great weights can be lifted. The member or " pillar " is forced upward beneath the load by means of a lever or by using the screw. It is held in position by a ratchet or otherwise when the motive force is removed.

Joinery. The finely wrought woodwork of a building which is put in after the structure is complete.

Joists. The horizontal timbers spanning from beam to beam, or wall to wall, to which floor boarding is nailed.

Knapped (of flintwork). Knapped flints are those which have been severed or squared by chipping. They are set in a wall to show the cleft end. This is usually black.

Lath. Slight strips of wood used to take the plaster of ceilings and stud-partitions. Tiles are sometimes hung from them.

Lap. The over-lay of one tile on another, or of one sheet of lead on another, etc.

Masons' scaffold. A scaffold that takes no support from the wall against which it is set, but which is made with an inner as well as an outer range of upright poles; also called an independent scaffold.

Mandril. A cylindrical rod round which metal is forged or a lead pipe dressed.

Metal-sheathing (of electric wiring). Wiring that is sheathed in flexible metal, usually in lead.

Mortise. A sinking cut into timber to receive a tenon, which is then secured by a pin.

'Munting. Any upright " rail " in panelling or in a panelled door which is fixed into the horizontal rails.

Needle (of structural building). A stout timber or metal beam passed through a wall as a temporary support for the superstructure, itself supported at both ends.

Piers (of structural building). An isolated mass of walling built to support a load.

Pig-lead. The commercial name for lead run into an elongated mould not yet cast or moulded for any particular purpose.

Piling. An arrangement of stout long timbers or ferro-concrete posts driven into the ground to stiffen it, or to form a base for foundations in soft or uncertain subsoil.

Pins (tiling). Metal or wooden pegs which are passed through tiles or stone slates whereby they are hung from tiling laths or battens.

Pinholes (of lead sheets). Tiny holes in a lead sheet which are difficult or impossible to find, due to bad casting or to long exposure.

Pitch (of roofs). The angle of slope given to a roof.

Plate (of carpentry). Horizontal timbers usually laid on or in a wall or other continuous bearing. They spread evenly over the bearing the weight of rafters or joints, etc., that comes on them.

Plinth. In masonry: a projecting horizontal course, usually moulded or splayed, set at the foot of a wall or architectural feature. In joinery: the same, but there usually called " a skirting," unless the architectural form is clearly derived from a stone-built prototype.

Pointing. The process of cleaning the outer inch or so from a mortar joint and refilling it with new mortar.

Principal rafters. The great rafters which form the upper part of a roof-truss (see truss). They carry the purlins, and usually at their feet are framed into a tie- or hammer-beam.

Purlins. The horizontal timbers which stretch from principal rafter to principal rafter. The purlins support the middle lengths of the common rafters.

Putlogs or Pudlogs. The timbers used in scaffolding on which the scaffold planks rest directly. In an independent scaffold these timbers rest on the inner and outer horizontal poles of which the scaffolding is made. In a " close " or " bricklayer's " scaffold the inner ends of the putlogs rest in holes left or made in the wall face. These holes are called putlog holes. They are usually to be found in old buildings; sometimes even they are left open.

Quoin. The corner stones of a wall, a buttress, or a pier.

Quarter turn, to (of bells). To rehang the bell from the headstock, turning it through one-fourth of a circle so that it exposes a new surface to the clapper. A bell is quarter turned when the clapper has worn cavities where it strikes the bell.

Rafters. The spars which form the slope of roofs. They rest at their feet on wall plates, and in their middle lengths on purlins. On them is nailed the roof cladding or the tiling lath. Medieval rafters are usually about $6'' \times 7''$ or $4'' \times 6''$, and are set to show the greater width below.

Rail (of panelling). The horizontal pieces in which the panels are set and into which the mountings are fixed. In a six-panelled door there are four rails. The bottom rail, the middle or lock rail, the upper rail, and the top rail.

Rebate or rabit. A square groove cut from the edge of a board or a timber so that the joint between two boards does not form a single plane. Where two or more rebated boards are set together there is an overlap in the joints between them, and at the same time their surfaces are in continuous planes. The word is sometimes used in masonry, as for the squared recess of a door jamb into which the door closes.

Reed (of thatching). In Dorset and the West, the straw of which thatch is made; elsewhere riverside reeds.

Ridge (of roofs). The topmost horizontal line formed by the junction of two slopes of a roof; hence the crowning tiles are called " ridge-tiles."

Roll (of leadwork). The rib-like joint between two sheets of lead, usually parallel or nearly parallel to the course taken by rain-water on them.

Roll moulding A continuous moulding which when it is seen cut across is found to form the best part of a circle.

Ropey-yarn. The trade name for the pitch-soaked twine used by thatchers in tieing down the reed.

Rubble (of stone or flint walling). That kind of walling in which the bed-joints are not coursed but where the stones, big and little, are laid irregularly much as they come to the waller's hands. Usually the face of the stone is left nearly as it comes from the quarry.

Sap-wood. The outer rings of a tree, just beneath the bark, which carry the sap to the leaves. It is particularly subject to decay. In oak it is of a lighter colour than the inner wood, which is known as " heart-wood."

Scarf (of carpentry). A form of joint between two timbers by which a timber may be lengthened. It is designed to resist cross, tensional, or compressional strains.

Screed (of plaster-work). Battens laid apart but in one plane, so that the straight edge of a board pressed on two neighbouring screeds and drawn along will give a perfectly true surface to the plaster or cement spread between the two screeds.

Shakes (of timber). English oak in large sizes as it seasons is apt to split longitudinally from the heart outwards. These splits are known as " shakes."

Shores. A word used in building operations for the raking or sloping timber props which are set as temporary buttresses to support a weak wall.

Shuttering. The temporary boarding or form in which concrete is cast to its permanent shape.

Sill, or cill. The same word as " sole," the bottom member of a structure. The sill of a window, of a timber wall; the sole-piece of a bell cage or the sole of a boot.

Silver grain. The medullary rays seen in oak boards or beams. These rays run at right angles to the rings of an oak-tree, therefore to display them at their best the face of a panel should be cut in a plane radiating from the middle of the log.

Soakers (of leadwork). The pieces of lead laid between tiles, slates, or stone slates, and turned up against a wall or chimney to prevent the entry of rain or snow. They are covered by flashings or by an oversailing course and mortar.

Spalling. The flaking of stonework, usually due to an excess of pressure on its surface.

Stagger, to. A technical term used of any repeated features when they are placed or formed alternately on this and that side of a line.

Straining-pieces. Timbers, usually of a temporary nature, placed to resist compressional strains passed from one wall surface to another.

String courses. Horizontal projecting courses of moulded stonework.

Struts. Timber props, usually temporary, and usually placed to transmit direct weights from above to a firm bearing below.

Styles. The continuous upright framing pieces of wood in panelling and doors into which the rails are tenoned and the panels set.

Swept valley (in tiled roofs). Valleys which are formed by interlacing the tile courses without leadwork or specially made valley-tiles.

Tell-tale. A dated strip of cement or other material set across a crack in walling so that when movement occurs or the crack opens, and it breaks, the change may be observed and the amount measured.

Tenon. A projecting piece left on the end of a timber or piece of wood designed to fit a corresponding recess (the mortise) in another piece, and there be wedged or pinned.

Tie-beam. A beam spanning a chamber from wall to wall, and fixed at its ends to the base of a pitched roof so as to resist the outward thrust of the roof and direct its weight straight downwards.

Tiling-lath. Lath nailed to the backs of rafters from which tiles, slates, or stone slates are hung.

Tilting-fillet. A strip of wood nailed at the eaves of a roof to raise a little the lowest course of tiles or slates.

Torching. Mortar laid on the underside of tiles or stone slates to check the entry of wind and blown rain and snow.

Truss. A triangular framework of timbers designed to carry loads. Thus roof trusses (of principal rafters, tie-beams, struts, etc.) support the purlins of a roof which in their turn support the common rafters.

Tucked up (of bells). A bell is said to be " tucked up " when the canon is let into a recess cut into the headstock.

Undercloak. The lowest or under course of tiles or slates at the eaves and verges of a roof.

Underpin, to. To underpin a wall is to build beneath it a supporting stretch of firm walling or foundation, without disturbing the wall itself.

Valley. The line formed by the junction of two slopes of a roof above a re-entrant corner of a house.

Verge. The edge of tiling or slating at a gable end where either covers the walling below.

Virgin pig-lead. Pig-lead that has not been used before.

Wall plate. The horizontal timber which is set on a wall top to take the feet of rafters.

INDEX

NOTES ON THE TEXT

See Introduction to the Reprint.

In all cases of named products and sources the reader should refer to the S.P.A.B. for current suggestions.

1. Now English Heritage (Historic Buildings and Monuments Commission for England), Historic Scotland, Cadw.
2. Now English Heritage (Historic Buildings and Monuments Commission for England), Historic Scotland, Cadw.
3. Parian cement is no longer available. This was a gypsum cement, composed of powdered gypsum, dried borax and cream of tartar, calcined and ground to a fine powder. It was used in the same way as Keene's cement which has also been discontinued.
   The monitoring of structural movement is now more accurate. Non ferrous screws and glued non ferrous dots can be used with Vernier callipers and Avonguard tell-tales (or similar methods of measurement with ready-to-read scales). These systems allow measurements in all directions of crack movements over a period of time. Glass and mortar dabs only record movement that has occurred at a particular time; this may be thermal as opposed to structural movement and action in the original position is not recorded.
4. 'Centres' or 'centering' as used in the construction of a new arch.
5. 'Acrow' type adjustable props are now universally employed for lightweight propping.
6. Down pipes and eaves gutters in cast aluminium may be an acceptable alternative to cast iron in situations where regular painting in unlikely to take place.
7. Archaeological advice should be sought before trenches are dug around this most informative zone.
8. A vertical damp course, as shown in Fig. 4, may, in some cases, encourage rising damp in the wall. Drains must be regularly inspected and cleaned.
   Failure to do so could result in saturation of the trench.
9. The risk of blocked outlets can accelerate damp problems in a building. See also footnote 8 and S.P.A.B. Technical Pamphlet No. 8 *Control of damp* by Nicola Ashurst, Gilbert Williams and Andrew Thomas and S.P.A.B. Information Sheet No. 4 *The Need for Old Buildings to Breathe*, by Philip Hughes.
10. Agricultural pipes are *more* likely to become clogged in clay soils.
11. Today the term would be reinforced concrete and the reinforcement would be mild steel not iron.
12. The misgivings expressed by Powys on steel embedded in concrete for remedial work to the walls of old buildings was well founded. For it is only recently that carbonated concrete has been found to pose a hazard.
13. Lime mortars for bedding may be suitable if monitoring shows that the wall is no longer moving.
14. Cement and sand grouts are no longer considered suitable for many historic buildings. They have been replaced with mixes compatible with a particular walling material. Low sulphate PFA (pulverized fuel ash) and lime mixes or pre-bagged mixes produced by specialist suppliers for different situations are recommended today.
15. Horizontal 'ties' formed from brick or tile are unlikely to be effective in resisting tensional or shear forces. If such ties are required they should be of reinforced

concrete with bars turned at the ends to improve the mechanical bond with the masonry.

16. Stainless steel can be used as a substitute for 'delta' metal.

17. See S.P.A.B. Technical Pamphlet 1, *Outward Leaning Walls*, by J.E.M. Macgregor.

18. 'Mathematical tiles'.

19. Concrete infill panels in a timber frame would not now be considered good practice. A lightweight panel should be used. Wattle and daub is an excellent lasting material even under adverse conditions. See S.P.A.B. Technical Pamphlet 11, *Panel Infillings to Timber-Framed Buildings by Kenneth Reid*.

20. See S.P.A.B. Information Sheet 2, *Timber Treatment* by Peter Locke and Information Sheet 3, *The Surface Treatment of Timber-framed Houses*.

21. Now known as 'plastic stone'. This is based on sand (or occasionally sand and crushed sound stone) as aggregate with a cement and lime binder, mixed as ordinary mortar; or hydraulic lime only with sand and stone dust. The mix should always be coarser, weaker, and rougher than the stone. Plastic stone should be limited to small areas.

22. See S.P.A.B. Information Sheet 5 *Removing Paint from Old Buildings* by Adela Wright and Technical Pamphlet 4 *Cleaning Stone and Brick* by John and Nicola Ashurst.

23. The pointing of brickwork should be flush or very slightly behind the face of each brick. Sometimes a slight hollowing or concavity in the joint is effective. See also S.P.A.B. Technical Pamphlet 5 *Pointing Stone and Brick Walling* by Gilbert Williams.

24. See also S.P.A.B. Information Sheet 11 *Rough-cast for Historic Buildings* by Andrew Townsend.

25. There is no longer a living tradition in decorative pargetting. Only minimal repair work should be attempted and this should be done by a good conservator. Records in the form of photographs and squeeze moulds should be made before work is commenced.

26. The use of heavy mineral oil for concrete now seems archaic. Water-proofing plaster is also wrong. See S.P.A.B. Technical Pamphlet No. 8 *Control of damp in Old Buildings* by Nicola Ashurst, Gilbert Williams and Andrew Thomas; and Information Sheet No. 4 *The Need for Old Buildings to Breathe* by Philip Hughes.

27. It cannot be emphasized too strongly that sound pointing should be left undisturbed, even if it has weathered back behind the general wall face to as much as half the height of the joint. See S.P.A.B. Technical Pamphlet 5 *Pointing Stone and Brick Walling* by Gilbert Williams.

28. The S.P.A.B. would recommend today a higher ratio of lime to cement for mortar in average conditions for the pointing of walls of old buildings. See S.P.A.B. Technical Pamphlet 5 *Pointing of Stone and Brick Walling*.

29. Sometimes garneting, galleting or garreting.

30. The correct pointing in brick and stone is to recess the mortar slightly leaving the arrises exposed. However local custom might suggest a procedure which could be copied.

31. See S.P.A.B. Technical Pamphlet 4 *Cleaning Stone and Brick* by Nicola and John Ashurst.

32. See also S.P.A.B. Information Sheet 1 *Basic Limewash* by Jane Schofield and Information Sheet 9 *An Introduction to Building Limes* by Michael Wingate.

33. Wakeley lime is no longer available. Contact the Society for sources of lime or the list of sources accompanying Information Sheet 9, *An Introduction to Building Limes*.

34. A strong bucket of any galvanized metal or enamelled ironware would be suitable. In practice it is more usual to make limewash by the cistern (80–100

gallons) rather than by the bucket (2–3 gallons). The limewash will improve if left to stand.

35. Salt is not recommended. Boiling water is not usually necessary when good fresh quick lime is used.

36. The interior of Henry VII's Chapel was limewashed by Sir Walter Tapper and the side Chapels by Peter Foster, MA, ARIBA, FSA quite recently. The cloister was limewashed by W.R. Lethaby and later by Peter Foster.

37. THE S.P.A.B. FULLY ENDORSES THE WARNINGS ABOUT CHEMICAL PRESERVATIVES ALTHOUGH THIS SUMMARY IS NOW OUT OF DATE. INFORMATION IS AVAILABLE FROM THE SOCIETY'S HEADQUARTERS.

38. There is a risk that the copper may stain the stonework.

39. The use of lead D.P.C's are not now recommended unless protected by bitumen such as 'ledcore'.

40. There is some debate about the effectiveness of capillary tubes. See S.P.A.B. Technical Pamphlet No. 8 *Control of Damp in Old Buildings*.

41. There may be a risk that alterations to a sub floor and bedding to the tiles will drive moisture up the walls.

42. Professional archaeologists should be informed when excavations are undertaken in order to monitor the site for historical evidence.
    Victorian encaustic tiles are now more highly regarded than when the book was written and should not be removed without careful consideration.

43. Temporary protection must be carefully designed to withstand wind. The scaffolding must be wind-braced and any corrugated iron or plastic roof should be secured with scaffold poles on top and not rely upon washered U-bolts.

44. Powys is probably referring to the heart-shake. Heartwood is less likely than sapwood to be attacked by beetle.

45. The use of steel needs to be assessed in relation to fire risk. Bolts etc should be protected with intumescent paint.

46. Mention should be made here of the use of resin in relation to timber-frame repairs. This system might merit consideration for small areas but only where traditional timber repairs are impracticable. A case for its use might be when it could save undue disruption of the fabric in the course of the work. The use of resin can deface the timber and cause condensation with subsequent rot and insect attack in the adjacent timber. It can also create a more rigid structure than was there previously. See S.P.A.B. Technical Pamphlet No. 12 *The Repair of Timber Frames and Roofs* by James Boutwood.

47. Galvanized steel brackets are, of course, very useful in general strengthening of timber connections, e.g. floor joists and beams, where joints have opened but are still sound and where reversal of the original movement is best avoided. See also S.P.A.B. Technical Pamphlet 12, *The Repair of Timber Frames and Roofs* by James Boutwood.
    S.P.A.B. Technical Pamphlet 2, *Strengthening Timber Floors* is a record of John Macgregor's own experience in strengthening timber floors. Every building problem is different and the S.P.A.B. would like to stress the importance of consulting an expert before this type of work is contemplated as methods cited may not be appropriate in a particular instance.

48. Xestobium rufovillosum.
    There is growing concern about health risks to occupants of treated buildings, and to building workers, caused by many of the products used by the wood preservative industry. Also, for the persistence of the toxic chemicals in the environment and the effects on wildlife, such as bats, which are protected by law.

49. Heppel/Kenford Ltd and the Disinfectant and General Products Company no longer exist. A permethrin based product may be suitable in many cases.

50. Merulius lacrymans, now called Serpula lacrymans.
51. The same health risks are applicable to the use of fungicides as for insecticides.
52. This is now a matter for specialist conservators and should not be attempted by the architect unless specially trained.
53. See S.P.A.B. Information Sheet 10, *Patching Old Floorboards* by Philip Hughes and S.P.A.B. Technical Pamphlet 2, *Strengthening Timber Floors* by John Macgregor (see note 47 above).
54. This is a practice which is not now generally recommended.
55. The regular painting of flagpoles is not always effective, even when the shakes are caulked, as water on entering a shake can become sealed and hasten decay.
    Pressure impregnated wood poles should be considered as an alternative. For Churches, a pole on the ground in a traditional tabernacle has certain advantages as it can do no damage to the Tower and would probably reduce the hazard of a lightning strike. (Powys does not discuss Lightning Conductors).
    It is necessary to comply with the current Code relating to Lightning Conductors if a new installation is required and any existing installations should be tested for satisfactory earthing on an annual basis.
56. The reader should check current sources of stone tiles in The Natural Stone Directory, compiled and published by Stone Industries.
57. Mr. Powys's advice on pantiles is sound. In certain districts old type pantiles on untearable felt have been satisfactory in the past, but birds have become increasingly destructive. In any event a second line of defence with boards and felt is essential against driving snow. Old fashioned torching might be possible in certain circumstances.
58. See S.P.A.B. Technical Pamphlet 10, *The Care and Repair of Thatched Roofs* by Peter Brockett and Adela Wright.
    Ramworth should be Ranworth.
59. Lead burning is now common and, when well carried out, is effective but the fire risk is very great particularly if undertaken over timber boarding. Close supervision is vital as many fine buildings have been destroyed from this cause.
60. Due to changed recommendations in the practice of laying lead and to changing conditions within some roofs and possibly also to the metallurgy of lead itself, there have been some disastrous failures to newly laid roofs. Research on the causes of failure and recommendations for future practice are still in progress. The best advice at present, (1995) is to relay the roof as before and only make modifications if there has been an obvious failure which is clearly apparent.
61. The S.P.A.B. has always deprecated the practice of substituting copper for lead both for the traditional and for the aesthetic reasons advanced by Powys and also because of the numerous and embarrassing failures of copper.
62. Came or camb.
63. Advice on the repair and protection of stained glass should be sought from the British National Committee for the Conservation of Stained Glass (Corpus Vitrearum), c/o the British Academy, 20–21 Cornwall Terrace London NW1 4QP.
64. The S.P.A.B. endorses the general views stated here, but points out that there have been several advances since. Cleaning should be entrusted to specialized conservators.
65. Expanded stainless steel lath will often make suitable reinforcement for valuable plasterwork. Fibreglass matting is also an established material.
66. Repairs to the screen at Hanborough Church, as shown in Figs. 37 and 38 were done by E.D.H. Crossley FSA not William Weir.
67. Pintoff and Parvo paint removers are no longer available. See S.P.A.B. Information Sheet 5, *Removing Paint from Old Buildings* by Adela Wright.

THE PROTECTION OF WALL PAINTINGS

WARNING NOTE

This chapter covers an area of building conservation where changes have occurred over the years. The techniques described here have proved to be unsuccessful and are now thoroughly discredited. EXPERIENCED SPECIALIST ADVICE SHOULD BE SOUGHT BEFORE EMBARKING ON ANY FORM OF TREATMENT, PRACTICAL OR AESTHETIC.

68. THE S.P.A.B. WISHES TO REINFORCE THE CAVEATS ABOUT THE UNCOVERING OF WALL PAINTINGS. ANY WORK ON A WALL PAINTING IS A JOB FOR THE EXPERT. METHODS HAVE IMPROVED GREATLY, AND READERS ARE ADVISED NOT TO TRY THE TECHNIQUES HERE DESCRIBED. OFTEN SUPERIMPOSED LAYERS CAN BE DETACHED AND SAVED.

69. Nowadays greater emphasis should be given to the overall treatment of the wall inside and outside. For instance, materials which reduce evaporation, such as cement and emulsion paint, should ON NO ACCOUNT BE USED IN THE VICINITY OF MURAL PAINTINGS.

70. METHODS OF FIXING MURAL PAINTINGS HAVE SUBSTANTIALLY CHANGED SINCE POWYS' DAY AND THE METHODS DESCRIBED HERE SHOULD ON NO ACCOUNT BE USED. USE OF SEALANTS, SUCH AS WAX, HAVE PROVED TO BE EXTREMELY HARMFUL.

71. Everseal paint and the Anthracite Radiation Company no longer exist.

72. See also S.P.A.B. Technical Pamphlet 9, *Electrical Installations in Old Buildings* by Alistair Hunt.

73. 'Bathrooms' for 193 read 192.
'Beam ends' add 120.
'Surroundings' for 194 read 193.
'Weir, William', add 195, omit 198.